Pondered in her Heart

For Phyllis Baumgartner
Sept 7, 2011

Hannah's Book: Inside and Outside

Elaine Sommers Rich

Elaine Sommers Rich

Wordsworth – Newton, Kansas

Library of Congress No. 98-84134

ISBN 0-945530-20-X

Unless otherwise noted, scripture references in the book are based on the Revised Standard Version of *The Holy Bible*, Thomas Nelson & Sons, 1952.

Printed in the United States of America
by Pine Hill Press, Freeman, South Dakota

To the following persons because of the way they have lived their later years:

Paul Adams, Jessie Banno, Ella Bauman, H.W. and Olga Berkey, Mary Bertsche, Blanche Burch, Gerhard Ens, Alta Mae Erb, Frank Laubach, Ruth Linden, A.J. and Alta Metzler, Paul and Lona Myers, Cora Nicodemus, Uncle Davy and Aunt Edith Richert, Chiyo and Gan Sakakibara, Gilbert and Cornelia Schroer, Iva Sommers, Noah Sommers, Milton and Lillian Sprunger, Lillian Steiner, Agnes Strouse, Maurice and Billie Troyer, S.W. Witmer, Olive Wyse, Elizabeth Yates, Harry and Jean Yoder, and Hachiro Yuasa.

This story is fiction constructed from the raw materials in the author's poetic imagination.

Like a braid, the book has three strands: Hannah Hershberger's life in her retirement years "At Shalom"; her past life as she records it "Inside Her Book"; and her earlier life as it appeared through the viewpoints of others "Outside Her Book."

> *. . . kept all these things and pondered them in her heart.*
> —Luke 2:19 (KJV)

Contents

Contents. continued

1. Which Comes First?

At Shalom
Hannah Considers Her New Home

Morning sun rays shining through an east window of Shalom Home highlighted the white hair of Hannah Elizabeth Shrock Hershberger, resident of Room 204, as she sat reflectively at her handcrafted walnut desk.

The flower garden quilt, my wood inlay "Tree of Life," my dove paperweight, *she thought.* All symbols of my life. Gifts from my parents and my beloved Daniel.

A window-shaped rectangle of sunshine brightened the blossoms of a multicolored flower garden quilt on the neatly made bed. Light shone on pictures of Hannah's children and grandchildren and on a faded, framed marriage certificate hanging on the wall.

At the top left of this old document were four red roses and an open book; at the top right, two doves and four more scarlet roses, roses which had once puzzled a child too young to express thought clearly. In the center a man and a woman dressed in vaguely grecian clothing sat in an open shell of a boat, presumably sailing across the sea of matrimony.

On another wall hung a wood inlay picture of a fruited tree put together in an intricate pattern of different colors of wood to form the fruited Tree of Life design.

1. Which Comes First?

As always Mrs. Hershberger had dressed for the day in comfortable shoes, a serviceable skirt, and an attractive blouse. She had breakfasted in the downstairs dining room, her usual cereal, fruit juice, tea, and toast.

She had read her daily morning Psalm plus a passage from the New Testament and had highlighted what was already much underlined. "This is the day which the Lord has made. Let us rejoice and be glad in it." "Little children, let us not love in word or speech only, but in deed and in truth."

Looking fondly at the photographs, she had prayed for every member of her far-flung family. Her oldest son Paul, his wife Ann, and their three children were the only ones who lived within easy driving distance. Peter taught in an international school in Kenya. Rachel Susan and Ken lived in California. Rebekah worked with a mission agency in Thailand. James, Michiko, and their two children lived in Boston. She recited their names in a prayerful litany, as she often did during a day. Protect them from evil. Make them a blessing to others. Grant them success in their work. Let your Kingdom come in their lives.

Hannah picked up from her desk a glass paperweight, held it up to the light, sighed deeply, and looked at it thoughtfully. A cube, the paperweight had inside it a white dove. When Hannah looked directly into it, she saw one dove. When she turned it slightly, she saw two doves. She smiled, set down the paperweight, picked up a pen and began to write in a spiral notebook she had labeled "My Journal."

I am an old woman sitting here in Shalom Retirement Home in the middle of the United States. I sit at the desk my father made and gave me on my sixteenth birthday more than sixty years ago. Today I shall begin my book. Will I finish it?

The Lord has allowed me to outlive my allotted three-score years and ten. Many residents here are older than I. Indeed some are nearing a hundred.

At first I was reluctant to come to Shalom, but because of the death of my beloved Daniel and the worsening of osteoarthritis, especially in my right hip, I simply could not keep up the retirement home that Daniel and I moved into after having lived in so many other communities. I deferred to the judgment of my five children and moved here. I am glad I did. What a relief not to have to worry about getting the lawn mowed or a broken furnace repaired!

During my lifetime I have seen and heard much. Now that I look forward to crossing the great divide between earth and heaven, I wish to set down some of what my eyes have seen and my ears heard. I still have so many things to figure out before I die, for example, how to cope with evil in the world.

A great advantage of living here at Shalom is that with no cleaning, cooking, or laundry to do, I at last have more time to write.

Writing does, however, present at least two difficulties. Already I am busier here than I ever dreamed I would be. I do not know how I landed on the Library Committee and on Shalom Residents' Council, but I did. Just now we have quite a controversy going about whether or not young people should be allowed to skateboard and rollerblade on sidewalks here at Shalom. I also belong to a prayer and Bible study group that meets each Thursday morning from 9:00 to 10:00. And yesterday Helen Hoover, the Shalom Activities Director, asked me if I would read to a blind woman, Ada Diller, in the

1. Which Comes First?

West Wing at least once a week. I could not say *no* to that.

A second problem is that watchful staff members expect me to follow the daily routine. If I do not appear at my place in the dining room at mealtime, some brisk young man or woman appears at my door to find out why. I don't want to say "because I am writing a book." I am sensitive about my writing and do not wish to be questioned about it.

These efficient young men and women are kind, but some of them treat me like a child and seem to doubt my mental prowess, which I do not appreciate at all. I may find walking difficult, but I can still think.

Rosie Basinger, my favorite aide, is, of course, an exceptional person. She treats me like a genuine human being whose brain still functions.

When I remember how much Rosie's grandfather Jeremiah Basinger wanted to marry me and how appalled I was at the idea, I can only marvel at the ways of the Lord. Or should I marvel at the ways of human beings? I wanted to marry Peter J. King.

Of course Rosie knows nothing about her grandfather's long-ago feeling for me, and I shall not tell her. Surely that is an old woman's prerogative. But that can be part of the book I shall write.

I do hope Rosie finds a job teaching music. Working here at Shalom is not her first choice.

Hannah closed the spiral notebook, took several blank sheets of paper from her desk drawer, and placed them in a ringed notebook. On the first page she wrote a title, "My Book." She paused a moment and then began to write her first sentence.

Inside Her Book
Hannah Begins Her Major Project

I feel overwhelmed as I contemplate what I am beginning on this day. I am writing a book, my first. I am writing it for two reasons.

First, I want to understand my life. Has it had a meaning? Has my life been worth living? Has it made a difference in the world? I hope so, but sometimes I doubt it. I lack faith. *Forgive me, Lord.* I want answers to my questions. Does God really direct the events in individual lives? How is it that persons marry whom they do? Why is there so little correlation between money and values? For example, why is taking care of children so undervalued in our society? Why does sex cause so much trouble? Where is history going? To Teilhard de Chardin's *Omega Point*? To the New Testament's *Day of the Lord*? Are they the same? What happens after death? What can one person do in the face of tremendous evil?

A second reason I begin my story is that I have a vague hope, a longing, that in some distant future a reader, not unlike the girl and young woman I once was, may find something on these pages that inspires her to joy or enlightens her about a person who lived through the amazing and terrible events of the twentieth century, yet remained strangely aloof from them, a pilgrim and stranger. The Great Depression. World War II. Auschwitz. Hiroshima. Stalin. Human beings walking on the moon. Television and computers. Famine.

I still understand little, although I am an educated

1. Which Comes First?

woman and have read much. Most of the pen wielding culture shapers of the Western world that I was required to read in university—Augustine, Aristotle, Kant, Freud—were men. They have helped me a bit in everyday life. *Beginning, middle, end.* That's helpful. *Our hearts are restless until . . .* Yes! *The starry heavens without; the moral law within.* That is also helpful.

I never could accept, however, that *id, ego, super-ego, Oedipus complex* stuff. Did any of those philosophers bring up children? Were any of them happily married? Until we have a happily married philosopher who is also a good parent and spouse, will we have an adequate philosophy? Perhaps that kind of writing already exists but has not yet been labeled as such.

I have often had to hide my learning, just as I now am sensitive about telling others that I am writing a book. I remember a time when I had to leave a room before the men present felt comfortable enough to discuss serious ideas.

People among whom I have lived have expected me to follow one of two patterns, either to be a homebody adept at child care, quilting, and cooking, but not at reading and writing, or to be a full-time career woman, placing my profession above all and looking down on the care of young children and the management of a household. I have fit neither pattern.

A dear aunt once asked me, "Why do you read so many books? It's not good for your little head." And a prize-winning reporter, M. Bea Dickenson, once asked me, "Why do you spend time ironing a man's shirt? You're wasting yourself!" Well I have tried to learn, as the Apostle Paul said, *in whatsoever state I am, therewith to be content.* In church circles it was all right to quote the Apostle Paul, in

12

academic circles Aristotle, in feminist circles neither.

But I must be careful of these digressions. I am getting old, and older people do digress. My present task is to set down as clearly as possible, events as I recall them while I can still think clearly. I do fear Alzheimer's disease. What I write here may be a race against time.

I shall begin at the beginning. I, Hannah Elizabeth Shrock, now Hershberger, was born following World War I in a village, Liberty, Indiana, to Susan and Mark Shrock, a humble, devout couple, rich in children, friends and relatives, health and happiness, but poor in this world's goods. I was named for my two grandmothers.

One of my first memories is of seeing my grandmother Elizabeth seated on a rocking chair with a newborn baby on her lap. This squiggly little creature trailed a pale blue cord. I was three years old at the time. Just that one mental snapshot. No memory of a cutting and tying of the baby brother's umbilical cord. No memory of a strange man, the doctor who attended the home delivery.

I have been present at conversations in which people shared their first memories. A theologian told of how he ran eagerly to show his mother the mud pie he had made and fell into an open hot air register. An educator remembered going out with her parents at night to see Halley's comet in 1910. My husband, Daniel, remembered seeing, from the safety of his mother's arms, a huge engine on a passenger boat in Lake Ontario. I could never participate in those conversations because talk of childbirth and pregnancy was not considered acceptable living room conversation.

Even if the subject had been acceptable, my vocabulary would have been inadequate to communicate the memory. I

1. Which Comes First?

have had teachers who said, "If you can't put it into words, you don't know it." That is simply not true. Reality is so tremendous that it is quite impossible, even for a gifted writer, which I am not, to squeeze it into words. I foresee that in writing my book, wrestling with language will be my biggest problem. That was my problem so long ago when I could not find the cherry picture for which I was looking.

Here Hannah looked up at the faded wedding certificate on the wall at the right of her desk. She gazed at it for a long moment before returning to her page.

I have experience first. Words come later, and they nearly always seem incredibly inadequate. For the heights, of what use is language? Although I have never spoken in tongues, I have known ecstasy in worship, in love, in listening to music, in the glory of the springtime. Joy? Rapture? Delight? Anemic all! And also for the depths, of what use are words? What could I say that day young Angela told me she was pregnant, or the day when I sat with my friend whose husband had fathered a child with another woman? What words can describe how I felt when Daniel died and I no longer wanted to live? Pain? Depression? Hurt? Agony? Feeble syllables!

What verbal label was I to attach to that mysterious blue rope-ribbon trailing my newborn brother? Years passed before I learned the term *umbilical cord*. As a young woman I determined that if I ever gave birth, I would carefully note the appearance of the umbilical cord to see whether my childhood memory was authentic. I did, and it was. But again I am getting ahead of my story.

Since I now may have only a decade or two to live, I must attempt the transmutation of all this experience. . . .

Suddenly Hannah Hershberger looked at her watch and laid down her pen. The Residents' Council would be meeting in just fifteen minutes! She was hall representative, and they had not only a controversy about skateboarding and rollerblading on their hands but also much planning to do for the Apple Butter Festival to be held at Shalom Home in just a few weeks.

How time flies when I am writing about the past! *Hannah thought.* But today is also God's gift to me, and I intend to live fully in it.

Outside Her Book
A Woman Finds Long Lost Cherries

A little girl lay on a bed in her grandparents' home, having been placed there for her afternoon nap. Hannah Shrock, for that was her name, had as yet only a limited coinage of words, but after perhaps a year and a half on planet earth, she did have a vast storehouse of experience. Everything she had seen, heard, and felt was part of her—the voices of her parents, the taste of oatmeal, the cold of winter, the sound of hymns sung in four-part harmony at her church. She did not say the names of her parents, but she experienced them, their love and caring, their delight in her. She did not say "canned peaches," but she knew their taste.

As the child lay awaiting sleep on her grandparents' bed, she saw on the bedroom wall across from her a picture containing clusters of what appeared to her to be red, red cherries. Cherries as bright as those on the tree at her home. Vivid red.

15

1. Which Comes First?

Through her tiny veins flowed something like a liquid joy.

Gazing at the red cherries in a happy glow, little Hannah fell asleep. She awoke, and was lifted to the floor. Later, the same day or at another visit, she wanted very much to see those cherries again. She searched for them, walking slowly through her grandparents' home, around a circle of dining room, living room, bedroom, kitchen, then dining room again. She scanned the walls of each room in quest of the elusive cherry picture. She could not find it, and she had no words to explain to the adults around her, her keen sense of loss, her acute disappointment. Hannah never found the picture with those cherries until many years later when she was a middle-aged matron and a mother of five children.

John Wesley Troyer was talking aloud to himself, as he sometimes did now that he lived alone in his neat retirement cottage, for his wife Sadie had died five years ago.

"July thirteen. My birthday! Thirteen has always been my lucky number!"

For decades his pleasant, resonant voice had both charmed and warned listeners in classrooms and in front of pulpits, for he was a retired minister-teacher. Now that his audience had dwindled to one, why should his voice be silent? He rather enjoyed hearing it himself, even though it was weaker, and he sometimes had to search for familiar words.

He continued his soliloquy as he settled comfortably into his armchair and picked up his well-worn Bible from the nearby table. "What will this birthday bring? Perhaps Susan and Mark will stop in a bit." His sister Susan and her husband Mark Shrock lived nearby.

He began to read Psalm 90, his "birthday Psalm."

*The days of our years are threescore years and
ten; and if by reason of strength they be
fourscore years, yet is their strength labour and
sorrow; for it is soon cut off, and we fly away.*

"They do indeed pass quickly," he commented aloud.
"I'm just a link in the generations. My children and
grandchildren. All those nieces and nephews."

Here he rose slowly from his chair, went to a nearby
window, and pulled the drapery cord just enough to allow the
sun's rays to shine on a small pot of parsley on a nearby
stand. "I haven't had a card from Hannah this year," he
thought. "I must ask Susan about her."

John Wesley Troyer loved all his nieces and nephews
but considered his sister Susan's daughter Hannah special
among them. Why? Well, for one thing, she nearly always
remembered his birthday, even from the other side of the
country. When July thirteen arrived, a letter or card also
usually arrived, often from a faraway state, for she had lived
in various communities, wherever her husband's forestry work
took them. *"With love from your niece Hannah."*

He and Hannah had their own private poetry game
they had played ever since she was a little girl. It went like
this. He would say, *This is the forest primeval, the murmuring
pines and the hemlock.* She would reply, *Bearded with moss
and in garments green, indistinct in the twilight. Longfellow.*

Or she would say, *Maud Muller on a summer day,* and
he would reply, laughing, *raked the meadows sweet with hay.
Whittier.* This uncle and niece loved many of the same things
—history, poetry, the Bible and its stories.

"Hannah would enjoy seeing her great-grandparents'

1. Which Comes First?

wedding certificate," John Troyer mused. "I wish I could show it to her."

He continued reading from the Psalms.

> So teach us to number our days, that we may apply our hearts unto wisdom. . . . O satisfy us early with thy mercy; that we may rejoice and be glad all our days. Make us glad according to the days wherein thou hast afflicted us, and the years wherein we have seen evil.

The doorbell rang, taking John Troyer away from his Book. Ringing that doorbell was Hannah Shrock Hershberger, quite unaware that during the next hour another bell would ring in her mind, giving her one of the most amazing experiences of her lifetime.

Uncle and niece greeted one another with joy. "Uncle John! I'm visiting my parents for a few days. And I believe today is your birthday." She proffered her uncle a loaf of freshly baked whole wheat bread. "Mama sent this for you."

"Thank you. It's still warm. How good to see you! Once again thirteen is my lucky number!"

"It just came out of the oven a while ago."

After a long absence uncle and niece mentally appraised one another.

"She's put on weight. Hair now has some gray in it. Looks more like Sister Susan every time I see her."

"He's aged. His hands are shaking slightly. I hope it's not Parkinson's. The room looks clean and orderly. He even tends house plants. No slovenly housekeeping odors. He's making it as a widower."

18

Hannah Hershberger, middle-aged matron and mother of five nearly grown children, settled comfortably into a rocking chair and prepared to listen to at least an hour of family stories. "Coming back to Uncle John's house is like lining up with the North Star once again," Hannah thought. "Wherever I go, this community is the place from which I get my sense of direction in the universe."

"I was just thinking of you, as I was looking at your great-grandparents' wedding certificate. Would you like to see it?" her uncle asked casually.

"Of course."

The old minister-teacher moved slowly to a nearby desk, opened a middle drawer, took out a framed document, and carefully handed it to Hannah. She examined it, and then was swept away by wonder. *The red cherries!* She felt incredulity and awe, for here in her middle-aged hands she now held what she had once searched for so diligently and never found, before she had words to explain anything to anyone. Now, here in her Uncle John's house almost a half century later, she had found those lost red cherries. She told her astonished uncle about her long-buried, prelanguage childhood memory.

She carefully scrutinized the old document. At the top of the marriage certificate were the long-ago-searched-for red cherries! But they were not fruit at all, but bunches of red roses, four of them at the left beside an open book, and on the right, two doves and four more scarlet roses. Printed on the certificate in decorative script and ink pen were the following words: *This certifies that the Rite of HOLY MATRIMONY was celebrated between Simon Troyer and Carolina Kendall on April 10th, 1870 at Miami Co., Indiana by John Shively.*

1. Which Comes First?

"Uncle John, this has to mean something!" Hannah exclaimed. "Is it perhaps that what we diligently search for we will find eventually, even though unexpectedly almost a half century later?"

"You were probably too little to see from the floor what you could see on the wall from that high bedstead. It was high." He laughed. "I know, because I can still remember a fall from that bed."

"Does it always take so long to find what we are looking for? *Seek, and you shall find.*"

"That's the middle of the quotation. *Ask, and ye shall receive; . . . knock, and it shall be opened unto you. Jesus.*"

John Wesley Troyer and his niece Hannah Shrock Hershberger shook hands at the end of their visit. When, if ever, would they meet again? Hannah, her husband, Daniel, and their five children were about to embark on a new venture far from her home community.

They played their old game. *"May the Lord watch between me and thee . . ." "While we are absent one from another. Deuteronomy."*

2. What Do We Remember?

At Shalom
Hannah and Ada Find Common Ties

Hannah Hershberger opened her spiral notebook, wrote the date on a page, and then began to write an entry in her journal.

Before I begin today's stint on my book I simply must record my extraordinary meeting with Ada Diller yesterday. Following Helen's directions, I found her room in the West Wing. She was expecting me. We introduced ourselves. She has had her eyesight most of her life but is now a victim of macular degeneration and sees only dimly.

First I read a letter she had received from her nephew, then news items of interest to her from our local weekly newspaper. I was ready to leave when she asked, "Would you mind reading a poem to me before you go?"

I was delighted.

"You'll find a gray book of my favorite poems on that shelf next to the window."

She chose Oliver Wendell Holmes's "The Chambered Nautilus." She listened intently, an enigmatic smile on her face, for she seemed to be seeing something or someone with an inner eye. I finished the lines.

2. What Do We Remember?

Build thee more stately mansions, O my soul,
As the swift seasons roll!
Leave thy low-vaulted past!
Let each new temple, nobler than the last,
Shut thee from heaven with a dome more vast,
Till thou at length art free,
Leaving thine outgrown shell by life's
unresting sea!

Ada Diller responded wonderingly. "The way you read that reminds me so much of a favorite teacher I once had. He made literature come alive for us!"

We talked further, and I was astounded to learn that that teacher was none other than John Wesley Troyer, my Uncle John. He has been dead for years, yet Ada and I, never having met before, sat in that Shalom room remembering him. I felt so excited and so connected across the generations. I certainly look forward to being with Ada again next week.

Inside Her Book
Hannah Remembers Eavesdropping

I have written about my birth, my parents, and my first memory. I shall now write something about my childhood. As I write at this desk my father made for me, I see on my bed here at Shalom a quilt my mother pieced and she and her friends quilted. It is a flower garden quilt made of forty blocks. Each block has an outer ring of twelve hexagonal pieces cut from cotton print cloth scraps. I love to look at those pieces—a small lavender check, tiny black flowers on a gray background—for they remind me of my mother's dresses and my own. At the center of each block is one yellow hexagonal piece, and between the center and outer ring are six pieces of Amish blue.

The quilt reminds me not only of my mother's sewing but also of how much I used to like to eavesdrop on adult conversations when the women did not know I was listening. I especially tried to ferret out whatever knowledge they felt was not for the ears of children. A clue to this kind of information was a sudden switch from English to Pennsylvania Dutch, the language my forebears brought from the Palatinate to the New World in the 1700s. People still call it Pennsylvania Dutch, even though it is not Dutch and is spoken more in Ohio, Indiana, Illinois, Ontario, and Iowa than in Pennsylvania. The adults presumed we children did not understand their childhood tongue, but I did. As I look back, I realize that the topics treated with this language switch were usually related to tragedies, sex, or the questionable behavior of others. Some would call the latter gossip, but I believe it was simply an illustration of a genuine interest in people.

For me as a child, though I did not consciously name it at the time, the trick was to become psychologically invisible to the adults, not to move or speak, to be preoccupied with a book or a game, and to seem totally indifferent to the adults. Ah, those were the ideal conditions for eavesdropping. Of course, one had to occupy an inconspicuous place.

Under the quilt frame was a great spot. My mother often had a quilt set up in our living room. Sometimes she

2. What Do We Remember?

invited seven or eight women in to quilt, a major form of social life for them. Usually the quiltings took place in winter during school hours.

Once when I got home from school, the quilters were still there. Always small for my age, I slipped under the quilt frame and lay on my back. I looked up at those flying needle tips coming down through the layers of cloth and batting, guided by a skillful left hand held under the quilt. And I listened.

"He's married already! Why, her body's barely cold in the ground!"

"It was just six weeks to the day last Monday that she died. I know because I was just about to hang out the wash when the phone rang. And it was my Elmer's birthday."

"Doesn't he have any respect at all?"

"A man should wait at least a year before he marries again."

"Yes, but it shouldn't be just exactly a year to the day, or people will talk."

"Well, if I die first, I hope my man does get married soon. He needs a woman to look after him."

That was my cache of adult information for the day, forgotten until many years later on the occasion when I rejoiced that I had not married Peter J. King, whom I once thought the absolute zenith of male perfection, not that he had ever so much as considered marrying me.

I myself never quilted until one day late in life. As a child I must have tried and either pricked my finger and got blood on the quilt or had dirty hands and soiled it. I do not remember. At any rate, my mother forbade me to quilt, and that prohibition hung over me unconsciously until one day

26

years later when I visited my father's old cousin Elizabeth right here in Shalom Retirement Home. Elizabeth insisted that "anyone can quilt." And I did. Elizabeth, unmarried, helper of many, is dead now, as are all my parents' cousins.

I look at the quilt on my bed and wish I had a cassette tape of all that was said as it was quilted. (Of course, cassette tapes had not yet been invented when this quilt was made.) What would I hear in the voices of those women long gone? And soon I shall no doubt join them. My mother's friends. They lived their limited lives in their small corner of the earth, creating beauty out of leftover bits of cloth. Would that I could create out of words what they created out of cloth, *a thing of beauty, a joy forever!*

Hannah Hershberger suddenly realized that daylight was fast disappearing. She glanced at her watch, then tucked her manuscript into a desk drawer. Tomorrow was the day she read to Ada Diller again. The next day was Apple Butter Day. A group of knowledgeable volunteers came to the grounds of Shalom Home annually and cooked apple butter in a huge copper kettle over an open fire. Hannah had agreed to help sell jars of apple butter to the many visitors who attended this event. It might be a few days before she got back to her writing. Walking gingerly, for her hip hurt today, she went slowly to the dining hall for her evening meal.

Outside Her Book
Elizabeth Quilts With A Guest

Cold rain fell all day. Would it change to sleet? Old Elizabeth peered out the window in her retirement apartment in the newly-built Shalom Home. Would anyone come through such weather? Her arthritis troubled her these days. And her driver's license had not been renewed when she was 88 because she had not passed the eyesight test. Giving up the mobility that went with driving her car was a severe blow to her independence. She could no longer go out to other people and events. They had to come to her. And they came too seldom. "Lord, do send me a visitor today," she prayed.

Old Elizabeth was finding it difficult to get into the mood for Easter this year. Other women her age had children, grandchildren, even great-grandchildren. Elizabeth had never married. Not that she had no proposals. Several men had wanted very much to marry her. When they asked her that crucial question, she also asked them a question. "I feel called by God to care for neglected children in our cities. Will you go with me?" When the men said *no*, she also said *no*. That was that. *The Lord is my husband,* she often said to herself.

As a young woman, Elizabeth did housework for wealthy families in town in order to support the nephew her own sister had abandoned. The nephew and aunt lived with her parents on a farm.

When the nephew became older and could support himself, Elizabeth went to work in what was called a city mission. In a poverty-stricken area of a midwestern city, she became part of a team supported by a denominational mission board that began what eventually turned into a small congregation. She started a Sunday school class for children. Sunday after Sunday she told them Bible stories, taught them verses of Scripture, wiped their noses, and wished she could bathe them and mend their clothes.

During the week she visited their homes, doing what she could for their beleaguered mothers, many of whom worked in a local cigar factory. Always she invited the women to the little mission church. They seldom came. She became accustomed to their excuses, or reasons, whichever they were. "It's my only day at home." "I've got to do my washing." "I don't have decent clothes." "It's the only morning we can sleep in." "My man won't let me come."

Elizabeth's religious garb protected her from molestation of any kind as she trudged the streets and climbed rickety stairs to third-floor apartments. On her head she wore a plain black bonnet. The skirt of her long-sleeved dress reached almost to her ankles. Over her shoulders she wore a cape made of the same fabric as her dress, fastening it at the waist with a clasp. The neighborhood tolerated her as a kind of benevolent crazy woman. Its residents became, in fact, quite fond of her in their own way, bringing her little tokens of affection from time to time—a hand-embroidered scarf, a holiday pastry.

Gradually, Elizabeth became convinced that she could not make a difference in the lives of these children unless she could spend more time with them. Daily she read her Bible and prayed, asking God for guidance in her life. One day an inner voice spoke clearly to her, *You must become a teacher. Leave here. Go to college. Learn Spanish. Get a license to teach.*

2. What Do We Remember?

I will be with you always, even to the ends of the earth."

Elizabeth borrowed money, went to college, learned Spanish, and got her teaching certificate. She taught in public school until her college debt was paid. Then she taught in Colombia, South America, and in Mexico, always under the auspices of her church, always on a mere maintenance salary.

But it was all so long ago. Elizabeth strained her eyes to gaze through the window at the dismal rain. She had poured out her life for all those children. Where were they now, the dark-eyed Juans and Juanitas? Grown-up men and women. And she was just an old retired church worker.

Perhaps one of her nieces would invite her for Easter dinner. The beloved nephew lived too far away. Perhaps she would eat with fellow residents right here in the Shalom dining room. Well, one day at a time. Easter would take care of itself when the day came. The joy and triumph of the resurrection did not, after all, depend on a dinner invitation.

Despite the rain and darkness she would not feel sorry for herself. *His mercies are new every morning. Great is Thy faithfulness!* She would spend the day quilting. That's what she would do. She had pieced this top from scraps given to her by a grandniece, one who sewed for her own two daughters but also had a full-time job and neither time nor inclination to piece quilt tops.

Old Elizabeth adjusted the floor lamp above her shoulder and sat down to her work. If her hands got any stiffer, this might have to be her last quilt. And her eyes were such a problem. She had to use a little wire device to thread her needle. Life did bring changes, she thought, as she stitched away and was soon plunged into pleasant memories of the past.

Cousin Mark had made this wooden quilt frame for her, with its two wooden ends, its two long rollers with denim tacked to them, and the wooden ratchets for rolling the quilt. This was the last such frame he ever made. He was dead now, as was his wife, Susan. All of Elizabeth's siblings and most of her cousins were gone, too. Only Cousin Moses, now 94, was ahead of her in age.

Where had the century gone? Good years they were for her, good years, despite all the trouble in the world. The wars. But life could be lonely at times.

A loud knock interrupted Elizabeth's reveries. Slowly she moved to the door, calling cheerily, "Come in!" Someone had come. Who could it be?

Carefully she turned the doorknob and peered into a shining face. "Cousin Mark's daughter Hannah! I was just thinking about your parents!"

"I am here for a few days for church committee meetings and stopped to see you. I'm sorry I can stay only an hour."

"Do come in and quilt with me."

The visitor stepped inside and began protesting, "But I . . ." for she was hearing a long-silent maternal voice, "Don't touch the quilt!"

Then she thought, *How ridiculous! My mother's been dead for years. I'm not a child.* She took a deep breath, threaded a needle, knotted the thread, pulled the needle up through the bottom of the quilt, and began stitching.

Two women, an older one and a middle-aged one, quilted for an hour, the guest apologizing often for her clumsy, uneven stitches, saying she had never been a quilter, yet feeling pleased that now she was one, the older woman

2. What Do We Remember?

disparaging her remarks. Of course she was a quilter. "Anyone can quilt."

The two laughed much and filled every minute with lively talk. The younger one learned details of family history she had not known before. The older one heard news of the world outside her apartment. Both women ended that day with a prayer of thanksgiving.

3. *Whom Should I Marry?*

At Shalom
Residents Enjoy Friends

Hannah Hershberger, resident of the second floor in Shalom Retirement Home, moved a bouquet of asters from her desk top to her bureau in order to clear space for writing. How thoughtful of Rosie Basinger to bring these flowers to me! She is a strange link to my past, *Hannah mused. She opened her spiral notebook and began to write.*

Apple Butter Festival yesterday was great. I met many of my friends from the community. Ada Diller and I went together. She said she especially enjoyed the smell of that apple butter cooking. *My nose still works even if my eyes don't!*

The time I spend with Ada really highlights my week. I read to her—letters, bills, items from the newspaper. Then we visit. Yesterday we talked about how difficult it is every day to meet people whose minds no longer function. She cannot see well, I cannot walk well, but we still have our mental faculties. Some others here have strong bodies but do not know where they are and cannot manage a daily schedule.

How do we relate to them? Do we have a constant feeling of pity? That's emotionally draining. Do we ignore them? That's not right either.

3. Whom Should I Marry?

Ada told me that one day she was sitting near the nurses' station on West Wing waiting to receive her medication. The woman beside her, very upset because she had just been prevented from going through a door, grumbled, "We're like animals in cages here!" Then she gestured toward the nurse behind the desk and whispered conspiratorially to Ada, "I wonder how much she gets for each one of us she captures." Ada said she wanted to burst out laughing. Instead she replied with mock seriousness, "Do you suppose it's as much as a thousand dollars?"

We concluded that perhaps the best method of relating to such people is to have a sense of humor and to accept them lovingly just the way they are.

The skateboard-rollerblade controversy rages on in our Residents' Council meetings. One side says it is simply too dangerous "to have kids speeding on our sidewalks. They'll knock someone over one of these days, and who will pay for the broken bones?" The other side says they do not like always being separated from the next generation. "It's fun to watch them skim along like birds flying." If we do not reach a solution soon, winter with its snow will postpone the decision until spring.

A whole range of activities is available at Shalom. Some residents like to play shuffleboard, lawn croquet, pool, or bingo. Others crochet bookmarks or bibs and baby booties to sell at the annual Christmas bazaar, coming up soon. What will it be like to have Christmas here instead of in the home where Daniel and I had lived together?

Hannah closed her journal notebook, then picked up the glass paperweight that rested always on her desk. She held it to the light, looking at the dove shapes within it, remembering the summer evening long ago when she received it as a first gift from the young man who later became her husband.

Inside Her Book
Hannah Wonders How Love Happens

How is it that I married Daniel Hershberger rather than someone else, Rosie Basinger's grandfather Jeremiah, for instance? He very much wanted me, but I simply could not return his feeling. At the same time, I thought I was in love with Peter J. King, who cared not one whit for me. I now realize that I did not even know Peter well. I was merely infatuated. I created a mental image with which I "fell in love." Such are the pitfalls of youth.

How anxious I was about myself as a young woman! I feared that I was unattractive to men. I was always more interested in ideas than in clothes. I foolishly thought young men cared more about appearance than brains, character, and personality. Daniel changed all that. In high school I could not get interested in basketball, Indiana's passion, nor in dating. I was interested in debate and was thrilled when our team got to the state finals debate tournament. The boys on that debate team were my friends. We had such fun together, but I never thought of them in a romantic way.

How does anyone ever know whom to marry? I love the Indiana story about the young man who in pre-automobile

3. Whom Should I Marry?

days rode his horse to the home of a young woman and announced to her, "The Lord has revealed to me that you are the one who is to be my wife." She responded promptly, "Well, He hasn't said anything to me about it."

I like John Woolman's chaste, succinct account in his *journal*:

> *About this time, believing it good for me to settle, and thinking seriously about a companion, my heart was turned to the Lord with desires that he would give me wisdom to proceed therein agreeably to his will, and he was pleased to give me a well-inclined damsel, Sarah Ellis, to whom I was married the 18th day of eighth Month, 1749.*

As nearly as I can explain it, that is how it was with Daniel and me. The Lord gave us to one another. One day we realized that we were moving inevitably toward our wedding day. The experience was not a stormy, being swept off one's feet happening. Rather it was slow, deep, quiet, sure.

For years Daniel Hershberger was just an older fellow in our church whom I barely knew. Because he was four years older than I, we lived in different psychological worlds, even though our parental homes were less than twenty miles apart. We went to different schools because we lived in different counties. He graduated from high school the year I entered.

Much later I learned how he spent the World War II years. At age eighteen he had to register for the draft. His lottery number came up. Then he appeared before his local draft board, asking for status as a conscientious objector because as a Christian he was opposed to war and killing. The draft board gave him a rough time, but in the end granted him 4-E status. He was assigned to a CPS (Civilian Public Service) camp at Medaryville, Indiana. The young men at that camp planted 55,000 trees on areas denuded by strip mining. Most of the men considered tree planting boring but better than dropping fire bombs on Germany or Japan. Daniel, however, had an almost mystical love of trees. The work he did at Medaryville led him to choose forestry as his life work. Later he was transferred to a camp in North Fork, California, where he helped do research on wildlife and forage at San Joaquin Experimental Range.

Meanwhile I went to college during the war, which was almost like attending a women's school. Then at last, after the bombings of Pearl Harbor and London, of German cities along the Rhine, of Hiroshima and Nagasaki, after the landing at Normandy, after the hell of the holocaust—Auschwitz, Bergen-Belsen, Buchenwald, Dachau—the long nightmare of war ended. Those who could, attempted to return to sweet, ordinary life. As young men from CPS camps and the armed forces flocked to our campus to get an education, I, just out of college, was drafted by our academic dean to teach freshman classes in the English department of my alma mater. I was overjoyed.

When in my twenties I became a college teacher, my friends began marrying. How did it happen? The thought of having a home, husband, and children appealed strongly to me, but I did not want as a husband the man who most wanted me, namely Jeremiah Basinger. He became a nuisance. He stalked me as though I were an animal he was trying to catch.

3. Whom Should I Marry?

At the same time, I thought I was in love with someone quite unaware of my existence, someone named Peter J. King. What was I to do? I thought I should do something. I was wrong.

One day as I read the Bible in a devotional frame of mind, Naomi's advice to Ruth leapt from the printed page and seemed spoken to me also. *Sit still, my daughter, until you know how the matter will fall.* I do not believe in opening the Bible at random and taking what first meets the eye as guidance. But I do believe that the Holy Spirit can use the written words of the Bible to provide insight to a seeker. That is what happened to me. I relinquished my burden of thinking I must decide whether and whom to marry. I turned it over to the Lord and continued my business of teaching.

A few years later Daniel and I met unexpectedly at a church-sponsored peace conference on a campus far from home. I was a faculty delegate from our college. He came from Purdue University, where by this time he was working on a doctorate in forestry. How glad we were to see someone from home! As I recall it, we listened to lectures about the destructiveness of the atomic bomb, and we participated in workshops on what we could do to stop the manufacture of nuclear weapons. I felt so honored that an older man like Daniel could be my friend. He asked me to write to him.

From that day on I saw Daniel Hershberger in a completely new light. I admired him for his knowledge, his humility, his social concern. Following that peace conference we corresponded for several years, writing about our views on religion, government, marriage, ourselves.

We began to spend as much time together as we could when we went home to visit our families at Christmas or for summer holidays. Both my parents liked Daniel. He and my father, a carpenter, shared an interest in wood. Daniel once said, "You know, trees have often lived in a neighborhood longer than anyone else." That delighted my dad. He took Daniel to see an old oak tree he had climbed as a boy.

Dad and Daniel had long conversations about the merits of maple, walnut, oak, poplar, pine, for various purposes. Daniel enjoyed woodworking as a hobby. It provided not only recreation for him but also useful furniture for our home during his years of teaching. When he retired, he went into marquetry, making inlay pictures like "Tree of Life," now hanging here in my Shalom room, his gift to me on our fortieth anniversary. But again, I am getting ahead of my story, for I was about to write about another gift, the first I ever received from Daniel.

One August evening at dusk we sat on lawn chairs under spreading maple trees at his parental Indiana home discussing the future. The lawn was framed on three sides by a hayfield, a woods and a field of tall corn. Daniel had with him a small, white, unwrapped box that puzzled me. What was it? Why had he brought it into the yard? I was, however, too shy to ask about it. By this time I had finished my master's degree. I said, "I'm trying to decide whether to go ahead for a Ph.D."

Daniel responded, "If you want to, that's all right. I'll wait."

At that moment I knew we would marry.

"I saw something at the Chicago Art Museum shop that I thought you might like," Daniel continued casually, handing me the small white box. In it was this dove paperweight, which I have cherished all these years. At times when

3. Whom Should I Marry?

storms threatened our marriage, it reminded me that we met at a peace conference, for we did marry, with the blessing of a host of relatives and friends. It was the Lord's doing.

How long ago it all seems! How intensely serious at the time! Now I can look at those events with so much more perspective. Jeremiah Basinger married someone else, happily so far as I know. At least he has a lovely granddaughter, our Shalom Rosie. I heard that Peter J. King's first wife died of cancer and that six weeks later he remarried. Neither Jeremiah nor Peter is still alive. Daniel and I had forty-two years together. I have outlived them all.

How does it ever happen? How does that mysterious moment arrive when both man and maid know without the shadow of a doubt, "We belong to one another"? Once as an adolescent I asked my mother, "Have you ever wished you had never married or that you had married someone else?"

She kept on peeling her potato and replied placidly, "After you are married, you do not ask such questions."

Here a knock sounded on Hannah Hershberger's door. In stepped a pleasant young woman wearing a blue and white striped pinafore over a crisp white blouse.

"Mrs. Hershberger, do you remember that you have a dental appointment this morning? The volunteer driver is waiting for you down in the lobby."

"Rosie! Thank you! I did forget about it. I'll get my purse and be right down. Have you found that music teaching job?"

*"Not yet, but I'm still trying."**

40

Outside Her Book
Hannah Receives Unwanted Attention

Miss Hannah Shrock had the uneasy feeling that Jeremiah Basinger, student, was stalking her as though she were quarry, a deer or rabbit that he intended to catch. Jerry had been in an English class she taught last year, an excellent student. He wrote a research paper on Tolstoy's contribution to the peace movement and received a well-deserved A. That should have ended it, so far as Miss Shrock was concerned, but it did not.

Hannah Shrock now lived with three other young women, also teachers, at what the students had dubbed the Nunnery, an old barn converted into an attractive domicile. Oaks and maples shaded its hip roof; a zigzag rail fence ran along its front; a Swiss cowbell at the front door alerted occupants to the presence of visitors; and a sunken fireplace graced one end of the space that served as living room.

Hannah and her housemates had been catapulted into early teaching by the force of history. On June 2, 1945, following the surrender of Germany on May 7, the U.S. Congress passed the G.I. Bill of Rights, granting generous financial aid to young men and women who had served in the armed forces and wished to continue their education. Many entered college who would not otherwise have done so. Conscientious objectors who had spent from one to six years in mostly-male camps doing "work of national importance," building latrines, planting trees, caring for patients in mental hospitals, also began coming back to Hannah's peace-emphasizing college during these post-war years.

41

3. Whom Should I Marry?

Where could a hard-pressed college administration find enough professors to teach this sudden influx of students? At Hannah Elizabeth's beloved alma mater the academic dean tapped on the shoulder half a dozen of his most talented, academically gifted graduating seniors, all women, and offered them teaching positions at the lowest level, instructor. One taught beginning business courses, another introductory music classes, another elementary education.

Miss Hannah Elizabeth Shrock, recent recipient of a B.A. with a major in English, felt overjoyed to be asked to teach freshman courses in literature and composition. Because many of her students were older than she, she insisted on being called Miss Shrock rather than Hannah, an attempt to gain in dignity and status what she lacked in age and experience.

The next years proved heady for Hannah. Not the least of the excitement was the presence on campus of the young men. Strongly attracted to at least half a dozen of them, Hannah spent many hours in happy company. She possessed a Miranda-like spirit: *Oh brave new world, that has such people in it!*

Dazzling company notwithstanding, Miss Hannah Shrock worked hard. She prepared for classes conscientiously, gave horrendous assignments, and zealously corrected grammar and spelling errors on student papers. The name Jeremiah Basinger appeared on one of her class rolls, one name among many. He did not, however, disappear when his class with her ended.

She would go to the library to do a bit of research in preparation for the next day's classes. Who should be there but Jeremiah Basinger? Always Jeremiah just happened to be wherever she was. He would look at her, nod his head in greeting, and smile, was it *shyly* or *slyly*? Or she would leave her office in late afternoon only to find Jerry Basinger opening the building exit door for her and walking along beside her, either silently, or clearing his throat and asking some question, such as, "Have you ever read Goethe?" Hannah answered these questions briefly, matter-of-factly, and walked on. "Only what we were required to read from *Faustus* when I took German." He often asked her to read something he had written, for example, a fourteen-page-long paper entitled "A Critique of Nietzsche's *Thus Spoke Zarathustra.*"

Did she have time for this? No, she did not. Could she say *no* to a student seriously interested in learning? No, she could not. She lived in a state of turmoil concerning Jeremiah Basinger.

Meanwhile Hannah's contemporaries began marrying. She attended many a bridal shower and wedding. Hannah assured herself that she could be quite happy unmarried for the rest of her life. She loved these students and teaching. But she also daydreamed.

If I ever do marry, what kind of man should my husband be? First of all, he must be a Christian. (That was sine qua non.) And I think he should be a minister and a theologian. He will probably play the violin. He will love music, will probably sing baritone. Everyone will like him.

At the Nunnery Hannah Shrock and her housemates hosted many a party for students where singing, laughing, and both merry and serious talk went on until just before mandated dormitory-closing hours when students had to leave. One Sunday afternoon at a Nunnery open house discussion on the vague topic "Being Christian in Today's World," Hannah

3. Whom Should I Marry?

met Peter J. King, headed for seminary and unapologetically planning to be a minister. Peter's gentle manner and warm friendliness entranced the entire group that afternoon. His humorous stories of civilian public service days charmed the listeners, especially Miss Hannah Shrock. Hannah's heart beat faster when, as Peter left the Nunnery, he courteously said to his hostesses, "Thank you for a most pleasant afternoon."

Who was this Peter J. King? Hannah found her attention perking up whenever she heard his name mentioned in some chance conversation. She looked for him in gatherings of the college community and learned where he sat in the daily chapel service. Did he participate in any extracurricular activities? If so, which ones? Surely he strongly resembled that dream husband Hannah Shrock had conjured up for herself. How could she get better acquainted with him? Gradually he began to acquire in Hannah's mind a superhuman aura. He was the ideal man, perfection personified. Handsome, brilliant, kind.

Meanwhile Jerry Basinger continued his pursuit. No longer in Hannah's class, he now came frequently to the Nunnery, ringing the door cowbell especially at mealtimes, usually on a pretext of seeking counsel on some religious topic from such wise young women. "I am having trouble with the idea of justification by faith alone," he might say. Hannah and her three housemates accepted these statements at face value and responded with mini-sermons to which Jerry Basinger listened with mock respect.

One spring Saturday morning only Hannah was present at the Nunnery when Jerry Basinger jangled the Swiss cowbell. She stopped shoveling ashes from the fireplace into a garbage can and answered the door.

Dismayed, she spoke hurriedly, "Oh Jeremiah, I can't talk now. I'm terribly busy. I've got to clean this whole place by noon. It's my turn, and we're having guests this afternoon."

"Let me help you," he offered modestly.

In that weak moment Hannah accepted his offer.

Jerry worked diligently, happily, finishing up the fireplace, dusting furniture, even mopping the kitchen floor. Hannah also worked. She swept, hung laundry out on the clothesline, squeezed lemons for party punch.

After about an hour, grateful for all that had been accomplished in such a short time, Hannah brewed a pot of mint tea and offered a cup to Jerry. They sat across from one another at the Nunnery table. He reached out his hand for the cup, breathed deeply, swallowed intensely, then said with much effort, "Oh Miss Shrock, you and I could have such a loving life together!"

His quarry had been cornered. Hannah reacted with anger and confusion.

"No, Jeremiah. No!" She was stunned. She was furious. She wanted to tell him to leave immediately, to find someone else. But she also felt guilty because she had taken advantage of his goodness by letting him do that housework. She had used him.

Fortunately one of her housemates returned from campus at that moment. Tension eased. Jeremiah Basinger left, head high, looking hurt and somehow wronged.

"What happened?" Miss Cohort asked. Hannah, crestfallen, told her.

"Look, Hannah. You've got to talk frankly to Jerry. Tell him firmly that you do not return his romantic feelings. Tell him to leave you alone. And don't be so soft about it.

3. Whom Should I Marry?

Make a boundary line, and don't allow him to cross it. You should never have let him into the house this morning."

Chastened, Hannah agreed. After that, she did indeed draw a line and firmly refused Jeremiah's attention. Hard though it was, she read no more of his long, philosophical papers.

Although she continued to share with her housemates her annoyances at Jeremiah Basinger, she kept her growing feeling for Peter J. King strictly to herself. Was Peter the one for her? How she hoped so. Life with him would surely be wonderful. He was going to be a minister. Did he play the violin? How could she get him to invite her out?

One day Hannah purposely loitered enroute to chapel so that Peter J. King might unavoidably overtake and walk along with her. Unaware of how much her question sounded like Jeremiah Basinger's Goethe question, she amiably asked Peter, out of the blue, "Do you play a musical instrument?"

Surprised, Peter J. King answered briskly, "Only the piano a little."

That was that. He seemed totally indifferent to her.

Mealtimes at the Nunnery were the occasions for all kinds of discussions. At lunch one day Hannah introduced that meal's topic. "Why is it that one person falls in love with another person who doesn't return the feeling at all?"

"That's not love. It's biology. It's infatuation. It's juices flowing. Love is what is described in I Corinthians 13. It's patient, kind, concerned about the welfare of the other."

"Well then, how do people ever know whom to marry?"

"Believe me, I'll know without the shadow of a doubt when the time comes, or I'll be happy just as I am."

"If it isn't mutual, it certainly isn't love."

"I disagree with that. What about God's love for sinners?"

"You have to seek God's guidance in so important an event as marriage. When the time comes, you just know."

What a tangle! Here were Jeremiah Basinger, doting on Hannah Elizabeth Shrock, who had begun to dislike him thoroughly; Peter J. King, on whom she lavished many a daydream, although he was, unbeknownst to her, engaged to a girl back home who was in nurses' training; and in the wings a scientist named Daniel Hershberger, about to receive his doctorate in forestry, who, neither violin-player nor theologue, would spend forty-two years of his life as husband of Hannah Elizabeth Shrock.

Eventually both Jeremiah Basinger and Peter J. King graduated and left campus. Peter married his nurse, went to seminary while his wife earned the living, and pastored churches in various communities. Absorbed in her own busy, satisfying life of child-rearing and continuing teaching, Hannah Shrock Hershberger nearly forgot about Peter J. King's existence until a day decades after her Nunnery years when she learned that his wife had died of cancer and that he had remarried six weeks later. She remembered a remark she once heard under a quilt frame and thought, "I must not judge. Perhaps he was unbearably lonely." Jeremiah Basinger married a school teacher he met at his first job. They had four sons, the oldest of whom, Jeremiah Junior, fathered a lovely daughter, Rosalind, sometime worker on the east wing of the second floor of Shalom Retirement Home, whose friendship Hannah Elizabeth Shrock greatly enjoyed.

4. Does Pregnancy Cancel Intellect?

At Shalom
Christmas Arrives

Christmas came and went at Shalom Retirement Home. Wreathes hung on room doors. (Lighted candles were forbidden.) Cards with faraway postmarks crammed mail cubbyholes. Florists delivered poinsettias. Special decorative favors, tiny candy canes or red gumdrop bells, appeared on trays sent to the hospital floor. Youth groups caroled through the halls.

This year Hannah's gifts to her family came primarily from the Shalom Christmas bazaar. In addition to her usual Shalom activities, she helped plan a Christmas party for East Wing residents. She continued to write. Often her journal entry was about her friendship with Ada Diller.

Yesterday I read to Ada Diller, "Mr. Edwards Meets Santa Claus," the Christmas chapter from Laura Ingalls Wilder's *Little House on the Prairie.* Ada's face just shone as she listened. She said, "I used to read that to my school children. I would take a tin cup to school to show them."

I asked her where she ever got a tin cup. She told me her grandfather gave it to her when she was a child. Her face was so beautiful when she said, "I can see that tin cup so clearly."

49

4. Does Pregnancy Cancel Intellect?

She may be physically almost blind, but her inner sight is certainly undimmed. How amazing that her favorite teacher was my favorite uncle!

Hannah spent Christmas day with three of her five children and their families in the home of the oldest son, Paul. Two of the five, Peter and Rebekah, were in Kenya and Thailand respectively in their helping ministries and could be with the rest of the family only through prayer, letters, and phone calls.

Hannah praised God inwardly all day long. Thank You for these wonderful people! Are they really my offspring! How blest can one woman be? *She was convinced that her five grandchildren were utterly brilliant.*

If only Daniel were here to see them, but I believe he does know. *Paul and Ann's oldest son Philip was home from college and had with him an international student from Japan who taught them all a Japanese Christmas carol beginning* "Sheep Fast Asleep." *The youngest grandchild, James and Michiko's Katie, played* "Silent Night" *on her violin. Presents were unwrapped, to the accompaniment of many ahs and ohs.*

All too soon, it seemed, her East Coast family, James, Michiko, and children, and her West Coast family, Rachel Susan and Ken, said their goodbyes and drove their rented cars to the airport, leaving her and Paul's family in the Midwest. "Mother, you're the center," *they teased.* "The rest of us are the concentric circles."

Hannah Hershberger received more gifts than she knew what to do with—stationery, stamps, bed socks, a box of chocolates, a jar of hand lotion, handkerchiefs, a UNICEF calendar, photographs. She graciously thanked each giver, but the next day, back at Shalom, she gave the box of chocolates and the hand lotion to Rosie Basinger, and any gift not immediately useful to her she soon passed on to other friends.

At the end of the Christmas day festivities Hannah returned to the peace and quiet of her own room. The noise, conversation, laughter, and much confusion had tired her more than she cared to admit. Her hip ached furiously. Her children were looking forward—Rachel Susan and Ken to buying a house, James to finishing a research project, James and Michiko to having their Katie advance in her violin lessons. Hannah also was looking forward, but she more than her children had unfinished business concerning her past and was eager to continue it.

Inside Her Book
Certain Men Have Difficulty Discussing

Now that the holiday season is over, I am glad to get back to my book. Sometimes I wonder what my life would have been like had I been born male instead of female. I am glad to be a woman, but it has not always been easy. I found that anger at patriarchal attitudes and actions was for me unproductive. *"Women should not be ordained to the ministry." "A woman should not be given a job if a man needs that job." "Women are incapable of abstract thought." "A woman's work is per se not worth as much monetarily as a man's work."* And so on *ad nauseam.*

I fared better slithering around such attitudes rather

4. Does Pregnancy Cancel Intellect?

than banging into them head-on. A line from an old poem says, *Strive not, thou earthen pot, to break the wall!* I would have broken myself rather than the wall if I had hurled myself against some of those walls.

Once Daniel called a meeting of five or six friends and colleagues, all men, to discuss the state of the college where he taught botany for a time. How were academic standards to be maintained? Should the men themselves do something constructive to help? Endow a chair? Send a delegation to the governing board? These men, one of them an obstetrician, assembled in our living room.

I was expecting one of our five children, was about eight months along and felt huge. I wore one of those tent maternity dresses. Along with Daniel, I welcomed each of our guests, gave them hangers for their topcoats, and brought to the coffee table the requisite tray of refreshments. Then I found a comfortable chair in the circle and prepared to add my ideas to the coming discussion. Although I never spoke of it, I had a master's degree with a major in English and a minor in higher education and was as interested in the future of that college as any of them.

The men hemmed and hawed. They cleared their throats. They made perfunctory remarks about the weather. They failed to respond to my husband's lead questions and seemed distinctly uncomfortable. What was wrong with these men? They had been so eager to talk. Now they seemed to be waiting for something. The obstetrician crossed his right leg over his left and shook his right foot nervously. At that moment it dawned on me that these men felt psychologically incapable of having a serious intellectual discussion in the presence of a very pregnant woman.

I quietly left the room, closing the door behind me. Soon they were arguing vigorously, noisily. Should they raise more scholarship money? Should they advocate that admission standards be raised? Certainly students should not be admitted on the basis of athletic prowess only! *Wait a minute! We've got to have good athletes, and athletes can learn too.* So on until midnight.

I've pondered that incident a great deal. When I, the very pregnant woman, left the room, they felt free to talk, but not before. Was I some kind of jinx on their meeting? Did they think my mind had been turned off when my uterus was turned on? Did they think motherhood and mind cannot coexist in the same body? Were they afraid I might start having contractions there in the living room? What if I had?

I wonder whether times have changed. Or do such attitudes still exist? Come to think of it, I have outlived every one of the men who sat in the circle that night. That gives me a feeling of satisfaction. I have survived! But why should I feel so triumphant about it?

Often during those years I felt left out of intellectual and academic life. I felt isolated and on the periphery. But now as I think about my life with our children and their friends, I can see that I was short-sighted. I was not on the outside. I was at the exciting center of life itself.

Outside Her Book
Motherhood Proves Rewarding

In the early 1960s certain learned theologians said that God was dead. Hannah Hershberger had not noticed. She read professional religious journals with the feeling of a detached observer, isolated from the world of intellectuals. Although she knew the names of Heidegger, Sartre, and Gide in Europe, Hamilton and Altizer in the United States, she felt that none of them knew or cared that she or her kind existed.

Three times a day Hannah set the kitchen table for her family, including the baby, Jimmy, in a high chair at the corner. Within arm's reach of the table was a low bookcase that held cookbooks, Bibles, and a toaster. On the bookcase rested a wallpaper-decorated box into which Hannah had placed prayers written on three-by-five index cards. Her older children, Paul, Peter, and Rachel Susan, had helped her put flower stickers from the dime store onto each card. These simple prayers were divided into three categories: morning, noon, and night. When the family sat down to eat thrice daily, they all took turns leading in prayer. For their turns, the children selected prayer cards from the box. In the morning Paul, Peter, or Rachel Susan might read:

> *Father, we thank you for the night,*
> *And for the pleasant morning light;*
> *For rest and food and loving care,*
> *And all that makes the day so fair. Amen.*

When it was Daniel's turn, he would often say, "Let us pray silently."

Hannah's favorite was a prayer by Robert Louis Stevenson:

Lord, behold our family here assembled. We thank you for this place in which we dwell, for the love that unites us, for the peace accorded us this day, for the hope with which we expect the morrow; for the health, the work, the food, and the bright skies that make our lives delightful; for our friends in all parts of the earth. Give us courage, gaiety, and a quiet mind. Amen.

After breakfast the three older children would rush off to school, Daniel would go to his experimental plot, classroom, or office. Hannah was left with Rebekah and James to care for, dishes and clothes to wash, shopping to do, menus to plan. And she seemed always to be president of at least one community organization. The year she headed the PTA she lobbied without success for a school lunch program. She fared better with her campaign to get a library set up within the elementary school her children attended.

Responding to her children's eager minds challenged Hannah daily. Once Paul and Peter, out walking with her, marveled at the rapidity with which a downy woodpecker drilled into a tree trunk. "How many times does it move its head in one minute?" one of them asked.

Hannah's answer was, "We'll look it up." But when the books of neither Roger Tory Peterson, nor Herbert Zim, nor Anna Comstock provided an answer, Hannah relayed the question to Daniel, as was her usual practice with questions relating to the natural world.

"The boys are asking how many times a woodpecker moves its head in a minute. Do you know?"

Daniel's face lit up. "I have an ornithologist friend at Kansas State University who's working on that very question right now. Many things about the universe are amazing and still not known."

He then told the children about a woodpecker's remarkable tongue that can penetrate deep into a tiny drilled hole to extricate a grub, about its extra backward toe, and about the strong barbed tail feathers that anchor it to a tree trunk.

Hannah discovered with amazement that frequently experts in fields from Biblical interpretation to astronomy could not answer questions her children asked. And so she and Daniel gave their children the feeling that much remained to be discovered about the universe. Daily Hannah Hershberger found that much in life was "amazing and still not known."

One day she found the family volumes of the *Encyclopedia Britannica* placed end to end along the living room floor. Jimmy looked up and said soberly, "I'm making a super-highway." Another time she responded to Rebekah's urgent tug on her skirt, "Come! See!" Through a window Hannah and her little daughter watched a robin catch icicle drips in its bill.

As a child, Peter, ever a collector of words, would ask with a thoughtful look, his tongue lingering on the unknown word, "Mother, what is a *situation*?" Or "What do you call a *somersault* in the winter?" Or, said with the air of a discoverer, as indeed he was, "There are two kinds of *meet*—*meat* loaf and *meet* somebody!" When Hannah explained to the children that *Mississippi* was an Indian word for *father of waters*, Paul asked "What did they call *grandfather of waters?*"

One day Rachel Susan, not yet in kindergarten, sat at her small table scribbling on a piece of paper. Hannah looked at the circular scrawls and said, "Tell me about what you are making."

"I'm making a poem. It says,
> *When I eat pickles,*
> *my stomach tickles.*
> *Dee dee dickoly dickles.*"

Jimmy was once incensed at a Bible reading which ended, *He that hath an ear to hear, let him hear.* "An ear! An ear! It should be ears! Everyone has two ears!"

Rebekah, aged four, one night attempted to keep Hannah at her bedside as long as possible by extending her evening prayer. "I thank you for my whole house. I thank you for the kitchen. I thank you for the living room. I thank you for the porch. I thank you for the steps. I thank you for the outdoors cold. I thank you for the indoors warm." Ah, motherhood! Was she encouraging prayer or being manipulated?

As the children grew older, evening end-of-the-meal-times often became voyages of discovery, Daniel leading eager followers. They chased ideas all around the universe. When the conversation turned to mathematics, physics, or the intricacies of genetics, Hannah felt lost. Then she would get up from the table and begin clearing up the cooking clutter.

When the children grew up, Hannah Elizabeth Shrock Hershberger looked at them with amazement, as though they

4. Does Pregnancy Cancel Intellect?

were strangers. The things they did, said, wrote about!

Had they really come through her body? Had she really once known all about them? She could not understand the things they wrote. Jimmy's *Elimination of Postsynaptic Sites during Axonal Competition at Reinnervated Neuro-Muscular Junctions.* Peter's *A Lefschetz Theorem on Foliated Manifolds.* International trade and monetary agreements. Seminars in Germany, South Africa, Japan. A breakthrough in immunology. Data base. COBOL.

And then grandchildren, wonder of wonders! With them Hannah experienced again the mysterious cycle of growth. Before she moved to Shalom, she had a children's nook in an open space under a stairway, where she arranged games, puzzles, and books invitingly, especially for Paul and Anne's children. Once grandson Philip, then about five years old, brought Hannah a book, looked up at her with a winsome smile and big innocent eyes and said, "Grandma, let's read about Pooh Bear," As she sat on the davenport, a little boy snuggled beside her, and began to read aloud again about Christopher Robin and his small friends, she felt quick tears of joy! How like his father! Hannah understood and delighted in her grandchildren.

She remembered a verse in Proverbs: "Grandchildren are the crown of the aged." "True, true!" she thought.

At Shalom a woman crowned with white hair, unconsciously rubbing her right hip, found in the bottom of a stationery box a grease-spotted index card with a blue hyacinth sticker on it. She smiled with reminiscence and read aloud from it with no one listening but God, whose existence she did not doubt, Give us courage, gaiety, and the quiet mind. Amen.

5. Am I Born Again?

At Shalom
Ada and Hannah Walk Through Spring

Although walking required the aid of a cane, Hannah Hersh-berger went for a daily stroll whenever weather permitted and also watched the coming of spring from her second floor window at Shalom Home. She observed carefully branches of maple, the pale green droopy flowers, the tiny furled leaves.

"Ye forest leaves, how green and tender, that shout for joy in springtime air," *she quoted from the old hymn,* "O that I had a thousand voices," *altering the line to fit the season.*

Sometimes her friend Ada accompanied Hannah on this daily stroll. Together they ambled along Shalom paths, past flower beds of daffodils, tulips, and hyacinths, Ada's right hand resting lightly on Hannah's left arm. Hannah's movements were slightly uneven, for she placed part of her weight on the cane in her right hand. "I like to feel the breeze on my face," *Ada would say.*

The Shalom rollerblade-skateboard controversy had been settled at last. Rollerbladers and skateboarders were permitted on the two long entryway sidewalks, but not on sidewalks along the building wings or between the cottages. The reasoning behind this decision was that since Shalom was tax-exempt and received some tax funds, it should give something back to the community.

5. Am I Born Again?

One day as Hannah and Ada sat on a bench near the entry bed of tulips, two boys, grinning broadly, sped by on their skateboards and waved at the two old women. Hannah described to Ada their haircuts and T-shirts. I may have taught their parents or grandparents, *Ada mused.* How good it feels to be in touch with the next generation.

When she returned to her room, Hannah wrote in her journal.

Ada and I just had a lovely walk. I never tire of spring. I grow old, but always springtime is new and speaks to me of new life.

We had another death last night. At Shalom we think more about death than about new life and birth, but today I intend to write about birth, the new birth. Is death also birth? I am not afraid of death. I think moving from this world into the next will be like moving from my mother's body into a world so dazzling, vast, and wonderful that I cannot even imagine it.

Inside Her Book
Hannah Remembers A Decision

Today I wish to consider my own conversion and the meaning of the term "new birth." A child in its mother's body lives in a small world indeed. A child at birth moves out, not only into the hospital delivery room but also into a vast universe that includes the constellations Orion and the Big Dipper, and countless galaxies such as the Milky Way. How daring of Jesus to tell Nicodemus that he must be born again!

Is spiritual birth of the same magnitude as physical birth? A baby is born with a soft spot at the top of its head. The head bones are soft in order to facilitate the baby getting out of that small mother's body into the larger world. I once heard a woman say of the patriarchal structures in her church, "Some men will have to have their heads reshaped in order to be born again." Do we have to have a soft spot in the head to be born again? Do we have to have metaphorical head bones that are not hard, brittle, set—head bones that can move?

I have had no Damascus Road new birth experience. I am a Timothy, not a Paul, for I do not remember a time when I did not wish to love and follow Jesus.

In our church community it was customary for an imported evangelist to hold two weeks of revival meetings each fall. These were designed to encourage the faithful and to bring into the fold those, especially adolescents, who had not yet decided to become Christians and church members. At the end of the evening's persuasive sermon the congregation would sing softly an "invitation hymn." Perhaps it would be *Softly and tenderly,* an old favorite of many in our church:

> *Softly and tenderly Jesus is calling,*
> *Calling for you and for me;*
> *See, on the portals He's waiting and watching,*
> *Watching for you and for me.*
> *Come home . . . come home . . .*

5. Am I Born Again?

The congregation seemed to breathe and pray in unison, creating an intense emotional atmosphere. My spine can tingle even now as I play in my brain those old memory tapes. Never mind that I was already home, and that I did not know what *portals* were. For years, as a little girl, I longed to stand or to raise my hand in response to those fervent evangelistic pleas. But it just was not done. An unspoken social rule made it clearly understood that this invitation was for adults, not children. You had to be at least a teenager to become a full-fledged member of the church.

One year I felt I could stand it no longer. With tremendous courage I raised my hand during the invitation hymn. What a relief! After that meeting my Grandfather Shrock asked me, "How old are you?" He had too many grandchildren to keep track of all their ever-changing ages.

"Twelve," I replied.

"You are just as old as Jesus was when in the Temple He said, *I must be about my father's business.*" How I treasure those words even after all these decades!

My life did not suddenly change that night, but its direction was set. For me being born again resembled a baby's becoming more and more aware of its new world. Each year I learned, am still learning, more about the spiritual, the transcendent, the infinite world of God's Kingdom.

People consider it a miracle when a mature man or woman turns from a life of gross sin, perhaps prostitution, alcohol abuse, or debauchery, to an entirely new life of love, purity, service, this through the power of God. It is a miracle.

But is it not a greater miracle to be kept in the first place from gross sin for an entire lifetime, this through the power of God? I know that I have often committed such sins

62

as envy, anger, jealousy, pride. I have confessed them and am forgiven. My miracle is that my body has been saved from being scarred by sin, for which I praise God.

The spring after I raised my hand in that revival meeting, after a winter of weekly instruction classes in Christian doctrine, I was baptized in the church. Some in that class were baptized in a nearby stream. We could choose which we preferred. I did not want to get my new white shoes wet by stepping into the water, which must reveal something about the level of my immaturity as a young girl.

Baptism is the symbol of a clear conscience before God, my Grandfather Shrock often said, referring to I Peter 3:21. So it was for me.

Unfortunately, the term *born-again Christian* became negatively charged during my lifetime. It became associated with ignorance: "God created the universe in six 24-hour days in 4004 B.C."; with narrow-mindedness: *"If you do not believe as I do, you will go to hell."* No one wishes to be associated with such viewpoints. I certainly do not. But what a pity that a beautiful concept, being born again, has become so sullied!

I wonder how Jesus came to understand childbirth so well. He said, *A woman giving birth to a child has pain because her time has come, but when her baby is born, she forgets the anguish because of her joy that a child is born into the world.* Did he as a boy live with his mother Mary through the birth of younger siblings? Did he have a beloved sister or woman friend who gave birth? Why did Dr. Luke not record Jesus' words about childbirth? Thank God for the Apostle John!

Here at Shalom Home we are far from the experience of giving birth. But we proudly display pictures of our grandchildren and great-grandchildren. We enjoy the babies and young children who come in to visit. Would that mine were not so far away and could come more often! Much as we enjoy the visiting children, we are glad we need not care for them twenty-four hours a day.

Outside Her Book
Hannah Gives Birth To A Daughter

To Hannah Hershberger these days seemed longer than days in the dim past when she had been Miss Shrock rather than mother-of-two, third-imminently-expected Mrs. Hershberger. *Count back 90 days from the first day of the last menstrual period and add seven days to that date.* Hannah had done that often, and she was now four days past due date.

"If our patients were not so smart, we doctors could simply add a month to that date and spare them these last days or weeks of anxiety," Dr. Slocum told Hannah at her weekly prenatal visit.

Weeks! Hannah felt impatient at the thought. She could not possibly wait weeks. Her suitcase was packed. Everything was ready for this child. The clothing to wear home from the hospital. A little undershirt. The diaper and plastic pants. An embroidered sacque her mother had made that would be all right for either a boy or a girl to wear. Hand-crocheted booties to match. Her own things were ready. A gown and slippers. A toothbrush. Birth announcements. Her Bible. A book.

And at home all was also in readiness. Clean clothes for Daniel and the two preschoolers, Paul and Peter. The shopping done, the refrigerator full of food. Arrangements for care of the boys should Daniel take her to the hospital in the middle of the night. How good of Mrs. Isaac to be willing to come at any hour!

The catch was that clothes became dirty and stomachs empty every day. Hannah could have everything ready for the Birth-Day when she went to bed at night, but by noon the next day the preparation had to be done all over again.

"Dr. Slocum," Hannah asked, trying unsuccessfully to hide her impatience, "Isn't there some way you can tell how close I am to delivering?"

"Mrs. Hershberger," he, also impatient, replied, "As I said, the head is down. Your cervix is two centimeters dilated. Does anyone know just at which moment an apple is ripe enough to fall? You are doing fine. I'll see you either here next week or in the delivery room." He left.

So it was back home to the daily routine. Each morning Hannah looked at the calendar and wondered, "Will this ordinary day become the special day I shall celebrate all the rest of my life?" She attended to the children, the household, Daniel, the community; cooking, cleaning, shopping, attending committee meetings, story hour for the little boys, worship services. People were extraordinarily kind to her, women friends inviting the little boys to spend an afternoon playing at their homes, offering to add her list to theirs when they went to the grocery store.

Hannah moved slowly, for she carried thirty pounds of extra weight. She ate lightly, for a normal meal gave her heartburn. She had occasional cramps and wondered whether

65

5. Am I Born Again?

they would develop into labor pains. Each evening her feet tingled, and she felt utterly weary. At day's end she prayed, *Thank you for this child. May it be whole and healthy. May I labor well.* And she fell asleep beside Daniel, grateful for him, her tower of strength. She wondered, *How could I ever get through a pregnancy alone, without the help of a loving husband and a caring community? Yet many women must do so.*

Then one afternoon as she moved faster than usual down the porch steps in order to keep her Peter from riding his tricycle into the forbidden street, the amniotic fluid broke through the membrane, and the contractions began. She brought Peter indoors and set both him and Paul down to animal crackers and milk, called Daniel, called Mrs. Isaac, and got her suitcase, in that order. *Relax! Relax!* she coached herself. *It's all quite normal and natural.*

The hospital to which Daniel took Hannah was known as "the hospital with a heart." Loving Christian nurses took Hannah's temperature and pulse, shaved off her pubic hair, washed her lower body, and timed her contractions. As the contractions followed one another quickly, they wheeled her to the delivery room. Daniel was allowed to don a white sterile gown and accompany her, for this hospital recognized that every child has two parents.

The great bearing down began. Hannah Hershberger pushed with every ounce of strength in her being. She thought of a sentence she had read somewhere, *The pains of childbirth are the most severe known to humankind. Yet women are willing to go through childbirth again and again because of its meaning.* In a mirror above the delivery table she could see the head. The crowning! Another gigantic effort of will and muscle, and the slippery baby popped out.

"Praise the Lord!" Hannah panted with relief and deep feeling.

"It's a girl," the nurse said.

"Wonderful!" Daniel's moist hand held Hannah's.

Such activity down there at the end of the delivery table, but Hannah was almost oblivious to it, although she did note once again that the umbilical cord was pale blue, thus confirming the authenticity of her early memory. Dr. Slocum cut and clamped the cord. One nurse wrapped the baby. Another cleared away the afterbirth. Hannah, euphoric and exhausted, was wheeled to her room.

When a nurse shortly brought the cleaned-up newborn to her parents, they counted her fingers. They counted her toes. They marveled at her nose, her eyes, her ears. What a miracle! They prayed a short prayer of thanksgiving to God for her and named her Rachel Susan for her two grandmothers. Then Daniel kissed Hannah's forehead and left to take the news of their new baby sister to big brothers Paul and Peter and to look after affairs at home.

The pain, the hard labor, were forgotten in joy that a tiny daughter had joined their family.

6. What Does Sex Mean?

At Shalom
Joel Visits Hannah

Hannah Hershberger smiled with remembered amusement as she took out of a brown envelope, delivered to her door by activities director Helen, a crayon-drawn picture of fish in a somewhat lopsided bowl. Wobbly letters labeled it MY GUPPIES JOEL.

The previous week a first grade class from the local elementary school had visited Shalom Home. The children presented a program for the residents, singing "The Wheels on the Bus" and other favorite songs. Then each child was paired with a resident for an "interview," a somewhat grandiose word for the conversations that followed.

Hannah's "reporter," a tow-headed little fellow named Joel, began their conversation. "How old are you?"

"Seventy-eight."

Joel's eyes grew big with wonder as he contemplated this number. After a thoughtful pause—"Were there still dinosaurs living when you were little?"

Hannah's eyes twinkled. "Oh my no! Dinosaurs disappeared millions of years ago." *She paused.* "We didn't even have television when I was little."

Joel considered this tidbit. "Why?"

"Well, TV hadn't been invented yet."

6. What Does Sex Mean?

"Where were all the TVs?"

"There just weren't any, because no one had thought of them yet. No one knew how to make them."

"I'll bet God knew."

"Yes, I suppose so. God knows a lot of things that people don't know yet."

Then an abrupt change of subject. "Do you have any guppies?"

"No, I don't have any guppies. Do you?"

So the conversation went.

A week later Hannah added Joel's drawing of a fishbowl to her basket of mementos on her bookshelf and sat at her desk to write an entry in her journal before beginning work on her book.

How rejuvenating it was to be with little Joel last week! He must be well taught, for he was certain of the omniscience of God. My guess is that he has wise, loving parents.

Joel's visit recalled to my mind the years with our children, and their births, each one so different. His visit reminds me that even though I am an old woman, I still do not understand sex, the act that produces every child that enters this world. In today's writing in my book I shall try to understand it. How is it that the same act can cause life's greatest joy or life's greatest pain and sorrow? Why did God design such a method for continuing human life?

70

Inside Her Book
Hannah Confronts Mystery

I believe that a child conceived as the result of the deep love of a man and a woman committed to one another in a life-long monogamous relationship is likely to be a superior child from the beginning. All my life I have hesitated to voice this opinion, but it is based on my observations. I believe it is in the nature of the universe that when people cooperate with God by observing divine laws, the results are better than when they disobey those laws. *In all your ways acknowledge him and He will direct your paths.*

Sex is part of God's good creation. I firmly believe that Daniel's and my children resulted from our love. I believe that children who result from lust, rape, or incest begin life severely handicapped.

Yet God loves every child, and we should as well. I used to sing with the children I taught in Sunday school, *Red, brown, yellow, black and white, all are precious in His sight. Jesus loves the little children of the world.* I think of Toyohiko Kagawa, accidental offspring of his father and a mistress, sent unwanted to his father's wife in the country. He was underfed, scolded, beaten. Yet he discovered the love of God and became a twentieth century saint. This is a possibility for every child. What a responsibility we have toward children!

Even though God loves every child, I believe it would be better if some of them never came into this world. When I read in the newspaper that a young mother shot her two young children, then put the gun to her own temple and pulled the trigger, I think of the words of Jesus in Matthew 18:6—". . . [I]t would be better for him to have a great millstone fastened round his neck and to be drowned in the depth of the sea." Perhaps it would be better for some people simply not to be living, never to have been born.

When abortion became a political issue, people asked me, "Are you pro-life or pro-choice?" How could I answer? I am both pro-life and pro-choice, as are most women.

Of course I am pro-life. I do not believe in killing. I believe in neither war nor capital punishment and certainly not in killing babies. But I could never insist that a young woman bring to term in her body a child that she did not want, resulting from rape. I am pro the young woman's life as well.

One of the vicariously most painful afternoons of my life was spent with a friend who had just learned that her husband, a respected churchman, had been unfaithful to her and had fathered a child out of wedlock. I thought, "If her husband had died, I would go to her, weep with her, support her. This is worse. I will go."

I went. Indeed it was worse than death. She sobbed to me, "If it were not for our children, who need me, I would have gone out to the railroad track and lain on it in front of a train. But I wept and prayed long. If my husband had come down with a severe illness, I would have stayed with him. This must have been an illness. I will stay with him."

And stay she did. I admire her. But I cannot understand how that man, her husband, whom I deeply admired up until that time, could have caused such pain to his wife, children, friends, church, and an innocent child. Can physical lust be so strong in a man that he temporarily takes leave of his senses and religious values? Was my friend right that it was like an illness? Are men and women so different sexually that I as a woman cannot understand that man?

Sometimes during my long life, as I saw nearly naked female bodies used to advertise everything from toothpaste to automobiles, I wondered whether this was a symptom of a great lack of loving sexual relationships in our society. When men and women think of one another only in terms of sex, they miss the great blessing of spiritual friendship, a richness I have experienced in the Christian community. Both Daniel and I have had many wonderful friendships with members of the opposite sex.

For us sex was part of the warp and woof of our lives together for forty-two years. Of course it was exciting when we were young, but it was best of all when we were past middle age, a sacrament of our belonging together, of literally being one flesh. I see sex as a sacrament of total lifetime commitment to one another. It has to be dedicated to God, or it will bring about terrible pain, cruelty, unhappiness.

As Hannah closed her book, preparing to go down to the dining room for dinner, the thoughts she had just written in her book continued. We may discuss whether we prefer broccoli with or without cheese sauce, *she told herself,* but we will not talk about sex, although I do believe the men at my table find me as a woman quite attractive. I like to be with them. And that is as it should be.

73

Outside Her Book
Angela Becomes A Mother

Angela's menstrual period had still not arrived. Never before had it been this late. Two or three days, yes. But never three weeks. Could it possibly be . . . ?

Angela tried to concentrate on her textbook. She had to pass her examinations. In fact, she had to finish college. Her parents expected it. Everybody expected it. She intended it. And she still had two more years to go.

Angela and Jack had been together in that way only once. Surely conception could not happen so easily. She had heard married women tell of how they had tried for years to become pregnant—had gone to doctors, taken their temperature every morning. It just could not be.

Of course she told Jack. They shared everything. What a man he was! How wonderful to be loved by him! (Angela did not question whether a man who really loved her would have placed her in this situation.) For the first time in her life Angela had someone who accepted her just as she was, did not criticize her at all, as her parents constantly did. Her parents were always harping on something. To hear them, you would think she had never done anything right. Thank goodness they were a thousand miles away. Jack told her almost daily how beautiful, fascinating, and brilliant she was.

Angela had come to this college because of Mrs. Hershberger, a woman who somehow became acquainted with her parents while Dr. Hershberger was working with the U.S. Forestry Service on a research project in Angela's home state.

It was scary and exciting to come to the great unknown Midwest for college.

Here she had met Jack and, in the proverbial manner, had fallen head over heels in love. Jack had everything —talent, looks, brains, personality. To her cupid-bewitched eyes, he was as nearly perfect as any human being could be. And he also was a totally misunderstood person. No one appreciated him—until now. He was orphaned at age six and lived with various relatives, longest with an uncle and aunt who considered him their duty. Two lonely young people were completely convinced that mere human beings could satisfy in one another that void that only God can fill.

Now life for Angela had taken an unexpected turn. Every day she looked in vain for a show of blood. She began to feel queasy in the morning and often lost her breakfast. She ought to get to a doctor. *That's what you are supposed to do.* But how could she? If only she could go to bed at night and get up next morning in the old carefree way—light-hearted, happy, in love with Jack, everything wonderful!

Instead, always this heaviness, this dreadful burden that would not go away. Perhaps she could get rid of it some-how. But how? And *it* wasn't an *it*! *It* was her and Jack's baby. Wherever Angela's thoughts began, they swirled into the same repetitive vortex. What to do? What to do?

By dint of sheer will power she passed her examinations. At the end of the school term Jack rented an apartment, and Angela moved in with him. She wrote to her parents that she had a job for the summer and would not be coming home. Jack did not understand Angela's turmoil. His solution was simple. "Let's get married! Right away! The sooner the better!"

6. What Does Sex Mean?

One day Angela went to the home of the only other person in that town who knew her parents. In desolation she sat down at Mrs. Hershberger's kitchen table. Soon the older woman seemed to understand exactly how matters were with Angela.

"You will have to tell your parents," she said gently.

"But I can't. I just can't."

"We have two telephones, one here and another in our bedroom. I'll stand by you on the other phone while you call."

At last Angela did what she dreaded most. She called her parents.

A strict father's ire, fearful to hear, scorched two pairs of ears. A red-hot voice burned, "Angela, how could you do this to us!"

"But Daddy," The girl burst into tears.

A voice interposed. "Mr. . . . please remember that there is a third person now, the baby."

"Yes." The hurt, angry man had not realized another person was listening. He could not yet comprehend the enormity of his daughter's news and said weakly, "Please help her, Mrs. Hershberger. You and your church. Please help our daughter."

For the next weeks Angela lived in the Hershberger home and made preparations for her wedding. She handwrote invitations. She chose flowers. She washed dishes and helped care for the Hershberger children. And she got to a doctor and began prenatal care. The church women agreed to do the wedding reception. Most of them had known Jack's parents, killed in a tragic accident when Jack was only a child. In many ways his life had been sad. The church people were fond of

Jack and rejoiced at his coming marriage, even though they felt he was too young to enter such an adult state of responsibility.

The hastily planned wedding went as flawlessly as if it had been in process for months. Angela's parents flew in for the wedding. Her cousin served as bridesmaid. Jack's relatives came from both coasts and from north and south. In a small chapel of the church, with traditional dignity, Jack and Angela were pronounced husband and wife.

A few years later Hannah and Daniel Hershberger returned for a visit to this community in which they had spent happy years. Leaving church on Sunday morning, they greeted on the sidewalk an attractive young couple, Jack and Angela. Jack carried in his arms a tiny, curly-headed girl, lovingly dressed in pink. Beside the parents an active little boy pedaled his tricycle. He had his father's clear blue eyes and his mother's fine facial features. Hannah Hershberger looked at him with overwhelming feeling and thought, "My first grandchild!"

The little boy, pedaling vigorously ahead of his parents, was heard to ask, "Who is that Mrs. Hershberger?"

7. What Does Society Value Most?

At Shalom
Hannah's Children Remember Her

Hannah Hershberger often thought of her children, whether near or far away. On Mother's Day she wrote about them in her journal.

My children are so good to me. I get letters from Peter in Kenya and Rebekah in Thailand every month. How they enlarge my world! This week Rebekah wrote, "Our work of rescuing young girls from prostitution in Bangkok is very difficult. What would I do without your counsel and daily prayers?" That makes me feel both humble and needed. My prayer group members pray especially for both Peter and Rebekah every week.

The flowers on the dresser are from Rachel Susan and Ken. They sent money to Paul and Ann to buy flowers for me on Mother's Day from the local florist. My "grandchildren basket" is almost overflowing with greeting cards, notes, and drawings.

And how thoughtful of Paul and Ann to take me to hear the Choral Society do Brahms' *Requiem* last night! Such music restores and revitalizes. Fortunately there was an elevator up to the auditorium.

Inside Her Book
Hannah Lists Her Priorities

Today I shall write about two conundrums I have never been able to figure out. Why is money received, so often quite unrelated to the social value of the service being paid for? And, how can a person earn a living by doing those services which really contribute to the welfare of society? It seems to me that if money is taken as the criterion, society's values are certainly topsy-turvy.

What is the top priority for a human society? Disposing of the dead is number one. We cannot have rotting corpses lying about. Undertakers (or funeral directors, as they prefer to be called, although it is the taking under that I am thinking about) do an important, urgent work. And they are adequately compensated financially.

Next in priority for a society I place helping women give birth. Midwives, obstetricians, nurses and their aides, all rank high in this my book. Are their salaries among the highest in a society? I doubt it.

Also close to the top of society's most urgent work is the care of babies and children. This seems obvious to me. The future depends on today's children. Yet when I compare an hour's pay for a baby-sitter or a day care worker and, for example, an hour's pay for a psychologist counseling a deeply-troubled teenager, I can scarcely believe the difference. Yet a baby that is held much, rocked, sung to, loved during his or her first year, from my observation, does not turn into a deeply troubled teenager. That baby turns into an adolescent eagerly exploring the world in constructive ways. Why then does the psychologist counseling the teenager receive so much more money than the loving infant caregiver?

Babies cannot lobby for their rights. They can, however, become permanently stunted or die from malnutrition. They can starve for lack of love and can turn to violence later in life unless that terrible void becomes filled with the love of God. Our society spends millions for tanks, bombers, all kinds of military defense. How much does it spend for the care and education of children? Why is child care at the bottom of the status and financial scale? That is my conundrum number one. All my life I have been trying to figure it out and still have not found a satisfactory answer.

I am a feminist, for I believe that every human being, female as well as male, should be encouraged to use her or his gifts to the full in any field of endeavor. But I do not agree with the kind of feminism which considers the present professions (law, medicine, the ministry, etc.) superior to caring for and educating children.

Because Daniel's forestry research took him to many different places, I have lived among all kinds of people. At one time we often had in our home as Jimmy's playmate, Dickie, a little fellow of seven, whose mother, M. Bea Dickenson, was a newspaper correspondent. In fact, she was part of a team that later won a Pulitzer prize for investigative reporting. That little fellow did not know that he should raise the toilet seat before urinating. At the table he held his fork and spoon baby-fist style. I confess that I felt critical of his mother for placing a higher priority upon her profession than on teaching her son the simplest things about everyday life. Surely she could have done both well.

81

7. What Does Society Value Most?

One day while I was ironing, Ms. Dickenson (she hated the title Mrs.) came by to pick up her son. She asked me rather scornfully, as I stood at the ironing board, "Why would you iron a man's shirt?" Both housework and the care and teaching of children apparently seemed to her unworthy of an educated, intelligent woman's time.

Once M. Bea Dickenson and I appeared on the same panel at a Women's Round Table discussing the role of women. That was fun. I enjoyed seeing the audience's reactions as I talked.

Back to my priority list. People must eat in order to live. Therefore I also place farming and cooking high on the list of society's priorities. Taking good care of the earth, air, and water, and planting trees—these, Daniel's top priorities, are also high on my list. Other good activities: manufacturing useful goods; creating beauty, as Daniel did with wood; all the arts; taking care of the sick and promoting health; teaching the Bible, especially the Gospels; any kind of research that increases human knowledge. Are these activities compensated adequately financially? Often they are not.

What from the point of view of values do I place at the bottom of my list? Pornography; operating brothels; manufacturing weapons; teaching people to kill; dealing drugs. I see the manufacture of weapons and the teaching of violence, for example, training Green Berets, as downright detrimental to society. I consider movie and sports stars grossly overpaid. I think we have far too many lawyers. Their existence makes for a too litigious society. I do not see a stockbroker making a contribution to society proportional to the financial compensation received. Destroying forests and turning fertile fields into shopping malls are low on my list.

Many professions should exist that do not as yet. We need conflict-resolvers and peacemakers. We need community builders. I can imagine future conversations like the following:

"What do you do?"

"I am a creator of community."

"What is your work?"

"I facilitate cross-cultural understanding."

A second Hannah conundrum: How can one earn rent-paying, food-buying money through such activities? Does the director of last night's *Requiem* have financial problems?

No one with money and political clout ever comes to me here at Shalom Retirement Home and asks, "My dear Mrs. Hershberger, have you any ideas about how we could bring about a better society?" But if they did, I would be glad to tell them, although giving good advice is also remarkably unremunerative.

As it is, I have been fortunate to get to work in the church, which is the frontier for the rest of society. Children are cherished in the church. Peacemaking is promoted and valued. The earth is recognized as belonging to the Lord. Canned commercial entertainment is discouraged. Although the church has by no means arrived at fully adequate practice on all these issues, it comes closer than any other institution I know of.

Hannah looked at her watch. It was time for her weekly Bible study group in the chapel. She was leader today. She laid down her pen, put her manuscript in her desk drawer, and went slowly on her way.

Outside Her Book
Hannah and Ms. Dickenson Are Speakers

The Hershberger dinner table provided a daily reporting time for family members. On this particular evening a frequent dinner guest, seven-year-old neighbor Dickie Dickenson, was absent. Daniel Hershberger sat at one end of the table, his wife Hannah at the other end. On one side of the table sat the girls, Rachel Susan, a freshman in high school, and Rebekah in sixth grade. On the other side sat the boys, Peter, a junior in high school, and James, second-grader, called Jimmy by his family. The oldest Hershberger son Paul was away at college.

Peter began the animated conversation. "We have our *Legend of Sleepy Hollow* TV script just about done. It's due day after tomorrow. Maybe the class will choose it as the one to act out at the school assembly. It would be fun to be Ichabod Crane. Does my head look like a pumpkin?"

"You're fishing for a compliment," his sister Rachel teased. "You want us to say you should play Brom Bones and win the heiress Katrina"

"Well, don't be disappointed if another script is chosen," the gentle mother admonished, "or if you have to play another part."

"I hope we have decent flashlight batteries by now," Rebekah interposed, for it was sometimes difficult to grab the verbal ball in these nightly conversations. "The last time I went camping the batteries conked out."

"I'll check them with my battery tester," her father offered. "When are you going camping?"

"We leave at six-thirty Friday morning."

Rachel Susan informed her family that she had a track meet on Saturday and that her oral report in government class on how a bill becomes a law had gone well.

James said they had a fire drill that morning and "a fireman came to our class and showed us his uniform."

"Well, I got a phone call today from the program chairman of the Women's Round Table asking me to be on a panel at a luncheon next month on "the role of women in society," Mrs. Hershberger announced. "Dickie's mother is on it too. They asked me because they want a conservative."

"A conservative!"

Daniel and the three older children laughed heartily at this, and explained to James the meaning of the word.

"They had also invited Everett Morris, the *Times* editor, but Mrs. Dickenson said she refuses to serve on the panel with a man. So they've canceled his invitation."

"Mother, you know she doesn't like to be called *Mrs.*!" Rebekah chided.

"Excuse me. Ms. M. Bea Dickenson."

"What are you going to say?" Peter asked.

"I don't know yet. Women are female human beings. The role of *people* in society. That's a whopping big subject!"

Hannah worked hard on her speech outline. On the day of the panel presentation she checked her appearance, hoping that nothing about it would distract listeners from hearing what she had to say. She drove to the hotel where the Women's Round Table met, found the Gold Room, and quickly concluded that she would simply have to put up with the cigarette smoke (for this was in the days when smoking was flaunted by many women as a symbol of equality).

7. What Does Society Value Most?

The program chairman met Hannah and Ms. Dickenson and asked cordially, "What would you like to drink?"

"Nothing, thank you."

"I'd like a bloody Mary please."

M. Bea's fingernails shone bright red. She had bluish-green eye-shadow above her eyes and huge onyx pendants dangling from her ear lobes. She wore trim black slacks and an attractive magenta silk blouse.

Hannah looked down at her slate-blue suit and wondered whether she appeared entirely too dowdy for this group. *Just how long are skirts these days? Why didn't I think to check? Too late now. At least I'm not wearing an apron. This is definitely not an apron crowd.*

Following the luncheon—chicken mousse, a too-limp salad and a too-hard roll, lime sherbet and a wafer—the women relaxed over their coffee and listened to the moderator introduce the day's panel on "The Role of Women in Society." M. Bea Dickenson, internationally known, highly acclaimed reporter, spoke first.

She began in her husky, melodious voice, "Women are an exploited political class. . . . A woman by definition has no life, no destiny, no identity."

Hannah listened carefully and studied faces in the audience.

M. Bea continued, "Marriage is a contract in the interest of men for receiving free sexual favors and unpaid domestic labor."

Why does she hate men so much? Why is she so opposed to marriage? She must have had some terrible experience.

Next M. Bea attacked motherhood.

"How do you account for the fact that two-thirds of all

86

new mothers suffer from postpartum blues?"

Two-thirds. Where did she get that statistic? Is it true?

"If being a mother is so wonderful, why do so many women reject it so violently? How often we read in the newspapers about mothers killing their infants. And this will continue until abortion is legal in this country." (For this was also before the Roe v. Wade Supreme Court decision.)

Poor Dickie! Does his mother consider him a mere nuisance, a hindrance to her career?

M. Bea Dickenson concluded with a rousing challenge to all women present to rise up and demand full freedom and equality. "Political! Reproductive! Economic!"

The applause was considerable.

Now it's my turn. Dear Lord, help me to communicate clearly to these my sisters.

Hannah arose. She looked into the faces of her audience—curious, skeptical, interested, bored. "It's only fair to share with you the assumptions from which I speak. . . . To begin with, men and women should love each other."

Now it was M. Bea Dickenson's turn to scrutinize the speaker. *Love! Mrs. Naiveté in person!*

Hannah went on to say that she considered monogamy the ideal form of marriage, that she thought every child should be loved and wanted. She favored family planning.

Every child wanted! Family planning! Tell that to the women getting knocked up like I did.

Hannah said she considered caring for babies and teaching children the most important activities of any society.

At least they are ways to stay poor.

"Baby-sitters should be paid at least as much per hour as lawyers."

7. What Does Society Value Most?

Yeah. Put that into a headline!

Hannah picked out the friendly faces and spoke to them. She said she thought that both men and women should have opportunities to do any work they wished to do. "If a woman feels called to run for president of the United States, she should certainly have the right to do so." She thought marriage should be a partnership of equals, that building a successful marriage required as much effort, hard work, and thought, as any other worthwhile achievement, such as getting an academic degree or succeeding in a business or profession.

Does this woman live in the twentieth century? What a dinosaur! I've seen her iron a man's shirt.

Hannah concluded by saying she would not consider it progress for the human race if women gained the freedom and equality in the military to fight in combat. "Rather, I'd like society to reach a level where men have the freedom not to have to fight. It would be better to teach men to be nurturers than to teach women to be soldiers."

How incredibly unrealistic!

Again the applause was considerable.

A third speaker, substitute for the male Mr. Everett, did a rather bland presentation of platitudes, and then the audience was given the chance to comment on the talks.

That evening at the Hershberger dinner table Peter asked, "Mother, how was your talk to the Women's Round Table today?"

"It was fun. During the discussion one woman said, 'I thought Mrs. Hershberger was supposed to be the conservative, and she was the most radical of all!' I admitted it."

The whole family, including Hannah, laughed.

8. How Does A Marriage Endure?

At Shalom
Hannah Attends An Anniversary Celebration

One Sunday afternoon Paul and Ann took Hannah to the fiftieth wedding anniversary celebration of the Smuckers in Fellowship Hall of their church. In the evening Hannah reflected on the event as she sat at her desk to write in her journal.

Daniel and I were not privileged to reach our fiftieth anniversary milestone, but we did have forty-two good though sometimes difficult years together. I enjoyed the Smuckers' celebration this afternoon but am always glad to get back to this familiar room. It has become home to me. Here I can think, pray, write. Here I have *shalom,* peace.

When I exert myself more than usual, as I did today, my hip always acts up. I hope it will not keep me awake tonight. I don't want to get addicted to pain medicine. The doctor says the cartilage in my hip joint has deteriorated somewhat. Movement in the joint causes pain and inflammation. He recommends that I simply take pain medicine when needed. Eventually I may need a hip joint replacement. That would mean a long stay in the hospital plus at least six months of recuperation. I hope that won't be necessary, but if it is, I'm sure I'll be given the courage to cope with it.

Inside Her Book
Daniel and Hannah Experience Difficulties

What should I write about our marriage, which lasted "until death did us part"? Daniel and I sometimes joked that our marriage was like that old riddle, "What happens when an unstoppable force hits an immovable object?" But it was no joke. It was agony and ecstasy.

Our marriage weathered storms. Its very existence demonstrated the grace of God—and Daniel. Once he said, "I think the devil is trying to destroy our marriage." Another time we reached such an impasse that at the suggestion of one of Daniel's assistants we went to a professional marriage counselor to get help. The counselor suggested divorce as the best solution for us. We did not want that.

We were both stubborn, independent, and creative. But we were quite different in personality: Daniel, an introvert, slow, deliberate, meticulous about detail, characteristics that made him a good researcher and a good marquetrier; I, extrovert, gregarious, impulsive, quick, talkative, ignorant of such basic forces in the universe as electricity, the rise of sap in the spring, and the movement of the earth around the sun.

Oh, I "learned" those facts in classes, but as Daniel and I rode along in the car, I would remark that the sun had totally shifted its position in the sky. It was now coming up behind these, not those, trees. Daniel would patiently explain to me the celestial mechanics of winter, and a year later we would have the same conversation. Or, Daniel would patiently tell me why different weights of motor oil are required by a car in summer and in winter. The information never remained in my head. I have never understood what goes on under the hood of a car.

I would look up from a letter I was reading and say, "How sad! My cousin's daughter's little boy died of a brain tumor. He was only five." Daniel would pause in reading the *Journal of Forestry* and ask with a puzzled tone, "Your cousin's daughter's little boy?" as though the syllables made no sense to him. I would try to explain to him who these people were, although next time he would not remember.

Daniel insisted that words be used accurately. He once jokingly criticized me for saying, "Paul has a temperature." "Everyone always has a temperature. Paul has a *fever.*" He considered *Mother* a respectful term and *Daddy* disrespectful because it is diminutive. He called himself *Dad* to our adult children and thought I should sign my letters to them *Mom* rather than *Mother.* Such a disagreement looks so trivial on paper, but in our daily life such differences sometimes grew to major proportions. Is that kind of thing typical in other people's marriages? Theirs always looked to me so smooth and conflict free, whereas we had disagreements about money, disciplining the children, food, entertaining, vacations, use of the car and other matters. We spent hours talking, compromising, working out our disagreements.

In the early years of our marriage I would meet out-of-town friends after our church service and say enthusiastically, "Come on home to dinner with us!" In those days I could easily cook up a delicious meal on short notice. Although Daniel was a charming, gracious host, this practice of impromptu entertaining upset him. He seemed to enjoy conversation if it was about politics, the environment or wood-

8. How Does A Marriage Endure?

working. He could discourse enthusiastically about kinds of wood most people, including me, had never heard of, like *padouk* from India or *narra* from the Philippines. He soon tired, however, of small talk about community events or people, while one of my favorite kinds of conversation was exchanging news about people. He said that I did not enjoy anything controversial or technical. True. Also, in my eagerness to speak I often interrupted Daniel unwittingly until I became aware of this bad habit and tried to stop it.

Daniel felt that I had no right to invite Sunday dinner guests after church on the spur of the moment without consulting him. In self-defense I would say, "Honey, I didn't know they would be there. And I couldn't find you."

The question of entertaining became one of many sore points between us. Eventually we gave up, I thought, quite a bit of it. But on Sunday noon I continued to use the good china and glass. Sometimes we ate mostly in silence. Then I would imagine the Lord Jesus Himself sitting at our table with us, just as He once sat with those travelers to Emmaus. I would feel blessed to be in Daniel's company. I would think, "I live with a great man. I should be satisfied." And most of the time I was.

Daniel would sometimes say, "Remember when we were first married and I was negligent in leaving bureau drawers open and socks on the floor? That bothered you, and I quickly changed my habits. Why do I still have to nag you to consult me about decisions that involve me?"

Once Daniel and I at my request went to the King Tut exhibition at the Field Museum in Chicago during a time when this magnificent collection of ancient Egyptian artifacts traveled from one American museum to another.

Waiting to enter, we stood in line for about twenty minutes, only to be told when we got to the entry door of the exhibition that we must check our umbrellas, camera, and briefcase. Daniel offered to do the checking. I promised to wait for him. But after a while I became impatient, felt I was wasting time, and went on into the exhibition.

Meanwhile, at the checking counter Daniel again had to wait in a long line. When he returned to the entrance, I was not there. I had not waited for him, and it took him a long time to find me. He was irritated. In the following years he often cited that incident as typical and symbolic of my breaking promises to him. He would recall that he had asked, "Will you really wait for me? Are you very sure?" precisely because this habit of mine had become intolerable to him. We remembered the incident somewhat differently. Now I hear him. Why couldn't I on that day? Now it is too late.

That same day at his request we attended at the Adler Planetarium, also in Chicago, a lecture in which the speaker told us that stars were still being born at the far edges of the universe, that light was still being created.

Now I can think of the museum and planetarium incidents in juxtaposition, as I could not on the day they happened. May light keep constantly emerging in all of today's marriages!

Our marriage seemed to me unlike those of others around us. I was sometimes tempted to envy them. Once I thought of an acquaintance, "How courteous he is to his wife!" Next thing I knew, he divorced her. I now believe that each marriage is unique and should never be compared with another. Even though I lived with Daniel for forty-two years, I never really understood him. Has God ordained monogamy because even a lifetime is not enough to learn to know fully another human being?

During the times Daniel and I were alienated from one another I would read Isaiah 54:5-7. *"For your Maker is your husband—the Lord of hosts is his name . . . [L]ike a wife forsaken and grieved in spirit, like a wife of youth, when she is cast off . . . For a moment I forsook you, but with great compassion I will gather you."* Of course, these words are a metaphor for Israel's rejection of God, but I found comfort in those sixth and seventh verses. Or I would sit down at the piano and play George Mattheson's hymn, *"Oh love that wilt not let me go, I rest my weary soul in thee."*

What did Daniel do at such times? He would go out into the night, look up at the sky, ponder the magnificent order in the universe, and think, "What are these petty troubles of Daniel and Hannah compared with such mystery and wonder?" Or he would go out to his trees and in his later years to his basement woodworking shop and make something useful or beautiful. Our marriage knew both bitter and bonny weather. We had forty-two years together. Too few!

We sat across the table from one another at mealtimes, discussing everything from the everyday details of our life together to current events and the meaning of the universe itself. Often we simply enjoyed companionable silence. We lay in one another's arms at night. We planned how to make our home more comfortable, then worked together to see our dream come true. We laughed together at funny incidents, like the time I mistakenly said, "I opened a *tune* of *canna*." We hiked through magnificent forests. We enjoyed hundreds of good times with our children and with our friends in the different communities in which we lived. To a widow

like me the list of good times seems unending and far out-
weighs any times of trouble.

Remembering Daniel's death still brings sharp stabs of
pain. So sudden! So unexpected! On that ordinary day, we did
ordinary things, but it became for me one of the most extraordinary days of my life. We went grocery shopping together
in the morning. While I put away oatmeal, canned soups, frozen juices, and prepared a simple dinner, Daniel changed a
burned-out light bulb in the bathroom, then went down to his
shop.

We always had our dinner at noon, a heritage, no
doubt, from our farm communities. That day we sat down to
fish, brown rice, tossed salad, and vegetables. Earlier in the
week I had made a special tapioca pudding, mixing into it red
raspberries which Daniel had picked and frozen the previous
summer. I spooned pudding into two stemmed, glass dessert
dishes and had them in the refrigerator. After we finished our
main course, I got up from the table, removed our plates,
went to the refrigerator, and was just taking out the dessert
when I heard a thud. Daniel fell forward onto the table. I
called his name. I called again. Alarmed, I tried to lift him but
could not. I dialed 911, and the emergency squad arrived
quickly, but too late. "Massive heart attack," they told me at
the hospital.

The rest of what began as that ordinary day is something of a blur. I was soon surrounded, engulfed, with the
lovingkindness of our children, of our church members and
neighbors. Paul and Ann stayed with me that night. Strange
that I remember clearly seeing the two uneaten dishes of
tapioca pudding sitting on the kitchen counter. They seemed
real—material, solid, tangible—while the events of that day

seemed unreal, like a dream from which I would awaken. I was still trying to comprehend a different order of reality.

What a jumble the next days and weeks were! Children and grandchildren arriving. Kind friends meeting people at airports. A viewing at the funeral home. (We suggested that people contribute to the local Tree Commission as a memorial to him.) All those people and the kind things they said about Daniel. The comforting worshipful memorial service at the church. I was grateful the sun was shining for the committal service at the cemetery. Could I have borne it if it had been raining? Yes, I could have borne it, but only with God's help.

During the next months came paperwork of all kinds. Insurance tangles. Lonely nights and days. And always just when I thought I could bear Daniel's absence no longer, the Lord would send me some kind of gift, and I could bear it. Perhaps the telephone would ring, and it would be Paul and Ann inviting me to their home for the evening meal. Or perhaps I realized that I could write a note of understanding to a friend who had just lost her husband, and the act of doing so would bring solace to me. I certainly could not have made it without the help of our children and a loving Christian community! Often I have reminded myself that Daniel did not have to suffer long difficult months of illness at the end of his life. I am grateful for the forty-two years we had together. Not every couple can celebrate a fiftieth anniversary.

Our youngest son, Jimmy, the only one of our five who shared his father's passion for wood, inherited Daniel's drill press, radial-arm saw, several sanders, and all kinds of precision hand tools. We sold the remainder of the woodworking equipment in the household auction we had when I decided to move to Shalom. I feel happy when I remember that many of the possessions that made our "big house" a home are now in the homes of our children.

Next month it will be just nine years since Daniel's death. Sometimes it seems it happened just yesterday. At other times it seems an eternity ago.

Outside Her Book
Hannah Meets Great-Aunt Mandie

Hannah Shrock Hershberger, graying, middle-aged, mother of five, sat in a marriage counselor's office unable to believe this was real, not a dream. She tried to fathom the words being read to her by Lucius C. Hampton, certified marriage counselor. *"If these conditions are not met by next April, a legal separation will take place, followed by divorce, Mr. Homer Hagerty to be the attorney."*

After twenty-five years of marriage Hannah and her husband Daniel Hershberger had begun to feel oppressed by one another. He blamed her. Why didn't she change? She blamed him. Why didn't he change? Gradually they had come to dragging one another down instead of inspiring each other to creative, productive work.

One day a former assistant of Daniel visited in the Hershberger home. Perceptive, he asked his host and hostess point blank whether they ever had trouble in their marriage. Being honest folk, they said, "Yes, a great deal." Well, he had

8. How Does A Marriage Endure?

a marriage counselor to recommend, "A fine man, a Christian, Mr. Lucius C. Hampton. If they ever needed help . . ."

That the recommendee belonged to their church denomination gave the couple confidence that perhaps he could help them. They made an appointment with Mr. Lucius C. Hampton, certified marriage counselor, and drove quite a distance to meet with him one afternoon. He talked to Hannah and Daniel together, eliciting as much information as he could about their relationship. Then he gave them each a personality test and a written quiz about how each perceived the other, collected these papers like a teacher taking up a test, put them into a manila folder, and asked them to come back the next week.

Seven days later he talked to each of them alone, asking what changes each would like in the other. Now, week three, he was again seeing each alone. Daniel had already had his turn while Hannah caught up on periodical reading in a waiting room. Now Daniel was reading his *Journal of Forestry* while Hannah entered the inner sanctum, an office which Mr. Hampton used two days per week.

Hannah noted that the name on the door of the office was not *Lucius C. Hampton*. When she read the nameplate, a flicker of her childhood home hundreds of miles away in Indiana, swept over her, but she was too absorbed in herself to notice, let alone analyze it. Hannah looked around. The usual. Two filing cabinets. A potted palm on the floor in one corner. A wide blond desk, behind which now sat Mr. Hampton. Framed certificates on the walls, plus a landscape calendar. And on Hannah's right, between her and Mr. Hampton, three pictures of children, arranged vertically, the kind proud parents everywhere love to display in their offices.

There sat Hannah Hershberger, a middle-aged woman, married to her husband for twenty-five years. In a chair behind a desk across from her sat Mr. Lucius C. Hampton, a man at least a decade younger than she. He read words to her that left her dazed. Was this real or a Kafka-like dream? In the line of vision between Hannah and Mr. Hampton, hanging vertically on the wall, were three framed pictures of children, two girls and a boy. That top picture of a girl about ten years old was about to become crucially important in Hannah Hershberger's life.

"Would you please read that again, Mr. Hampton?" Hannah asked, trying to understand the import of what she had just heard. Mr. Hampton reread the list of conditions.

Hannah Hershberger, head down, made an intense effort to listen to his words. "If these are not met by next April, a legal separation is to take place, followed by divorce, Mr. Homer Hagerty to be the attorney."

"I couldn't consider divorce." Hannah jerked to attention, straightening her spine, lifting her head. *As she did so, the eyes in a photograph hanging on the wall looked straight at her, right into her. Hannah gasped. What was Great-Aunt Mandie doing here in the marriage counselor's office? Great-Aunt Mandie had been dead for years. Great-Aunt Mandie was an aunt to Susan, Hannah's mother.*

Aunt Mandie and Uncle Abe had at least ten children—teachers, doctors, ministers, homemakers, farmers, all salt of the earth types. Hannah never really knew them well. As a child she saw them once a year at a family reunion and on Sundays at church, sitting with dozens of other old men and women, for to children, all adults are old. Now Hannah was quite as old as they once were.

8. How Does A Marriage Endure?

Uncle Abe and Aunt Mandie moved about the community a great deal. Were they renters, financially unable to buy their own farm? How did they survive during the Depression years of the 1930s? As a child Hannah never thought of such questions. She simply accepted the life around her.

Now she was wondering about Great-Uncle Abe and Great-Aunt Mandie as she sat miles and years away from the old home community trying to concentrate on the words of one Lucius C. Hampton.

"Mrs. Hershberger!" Hannah detected a distinct edge of anger in Mr. Hampton's voice. "You are an intelligent, well-educated woman! Do you mean to tell me you would not even consider divorce as a solution?"

Great-Aunt Mandie looked down from the picture at Hannah Hershberger.

I didn't remember that she was so beautiful. I thought she was fat. But she had to say something aloud to this man who was confronting her.

"If it came to divorce, I . . ."

Inside Hannah's head Great-Aunt Mandie whispered gently, lovingly, "Life isn't always easy." Dear old voices from the past joined her in a harmonious chorus. Masts. Shrocks. Mishlers. Hostetlers. Kings. "You mustn't give up." "Be patient." "Have faith." "God answers prayer."

Hannah tried spoken words again, looking steadily at Mr. Hampton. "If it came to divorce, I would feel I had failed my family (her voice trembled) and my church."

The counselor dismissed her curtly. "Come back next week." As she closed the office door behind her, Hannah Hershberger looked once again at that nameplate on the door. Then it dawned on her. The usual occupant of this office was a grandson of Great-Aunt Mandie and Great-Uncle Abe. Edna's boy! The pictured children were Aunt Mandie and Uncle Abe's great-grandchildren. How physical resemblances carry over from one generation to the next! And how the Lord arranges details!

Daniel and Hannah's homegoing conversation in the car was somber but salutary.

"He suggested divorce. I don't want that."

"Neither do I. He even suggested a lawyer."

"Do you suppose marriage counselors and lawyers are in cahoots with one another in order to drum up business?"

Two inwardly shaken people hardly knew whether to laugh or cry. They remained silent, trying to comprehend what had just happened to them.

They did not return to the counselor the next week. Instead, they moved, sometimes steadily, sometimes waveringly, toward their forty-second wedding anniversary.

9. Does Prayer Work?

At Shalom
A Prayer Group Meets

Once a week Hannah Hershberger met with a small group of women at Shalom Home to thank God for blessings they had experienced in their daily lives and to pray for their families and for peace and justice in the world. First they went around the circle taking turns listing their praises. These often included praise for health, letters and visits received, and good things that had happened to friends and family members.

Next they repeated the process, listing requests. "My sister-in-law just learned that she has cancer. Please pray for her." "My grandson has just been transferred by his company to Austin, Texas. Please pray that he and his family may find a church home there." "Rebekah asks us to pray for poor families in northern Thailand." "I need either relief from arthritis pain or the grace to bear it." Often one week's requests were the next week's praises.

Hannah returned from one such meeting to her daily stint of writing.

Life here at Shalom has been interesting recently. Next month promises more of the same, for the Residents' Council has decided that we will take a trip to the art museum then. Our activities director, Helen Hoover, is calling to learn the cost of entrance fees and the best schedule for us.

One great thing about living here at Shalom Retirement Home is that I do have time to meditate and pray, both alone and with others. This morning a woman in our prayer group, Mary Burton, related a remarkable experience. We have been praying for her very ill sister, Lydia, in Oregon. Mary said that last week following our meeting she kept lifting Lydia into the Lord's presence, at that inner level too deep for words. This is what she told us, as nearly as I remember it.

"Just as I was getting ready for bed—I was brushing my teeth, as a matter of fact, and not thinking of anything in particular—I looked up and all of a sudden saw the radiantly happy face of my sister Anna, who died twenty years ago. She was greeting Lydia, who seemed to be just arriving. Both had such radiant faces. I can't tell you how happy I felt. I fell asleep with such peace in my soul. The next morning, Friday, my nephew phoned saying his mother had died at 7 P.M. the night before."

We were all quite impressed with Mary's story.

Inside Her Book
Hannah Experiences Prayer

I believe in prayer, all kinds of prayer—praise, confession, intercession, contemplative nonverbal, whatever kinds there are. Some day people will understand how intercessory prayer works. For now it remains mysterious.

What if I could show my television set to my great-grandparents? I would say to them, "The air in this room is full of pictures and sounds. By turning this knob, I can show you pictures of what is happening right now in New York, California, Moscow, Johannesburg, Hong Kong, Lhasa. My great-grandparents would say, "It's not possible." What up until the twentieth century would have seemed like incredible miracles—airplanes, radio, television, space shuttles, computers—are now accepted as everyday.

Intercessory prayer is similar. A mother on one side of the globe prays for her son on earth's opposite side. At that moment a fog covers the son, hiding him from danger and saving his life. How does this happen? My Shalom friend Mary Burton's sister apparently died just at the time Mary had a kind of vision of her. I cannot explain it. I only know that it works, for I have had such experiences. The Lord once led me to our old Swiss neighbor Veronica Hilty, and it may have saved her life.

An acquaintance once told me he considered intercessory prayer "ordering God to do things, treating Him like a bellhop." I do not view it that way at all. I think of it as cooperating with God.

For many years I kept prayer notebooks. I had pages for Daniel, for each of our five children, for various relatives and friends. I also had pages for outreach works of the church and for world affairs. I wrote first-time requests in blue ink, dating them. As these requests were answered, I wrote down dates in red.

Later I kept one sheet of paper per week, and I still

105

9. Does Prayer Work?

do. I draw a vertical line down the middle, put praises on one side and requests on the other.

I discarded those old prayer sheets before I moved into this room, but one fell out of a book recently. I must have been using it as a bookmark.

Once on a March day I had listed these praises:

For life and health, mine, Daniel's, our children's,
For intelligence and creativity,
> *(Help us to use them in your service.)*
For a home to live in,
For a Christian community to be a part of,
For recurring spring: a pair of robins, a pair of
> *cardinals, tulips pushing up,*
For friends all around the world,
For the life of your servant Oscar Romero.

I also had a list of requests:

For Mildred dying of cancer and her family,
That Paul will find a job,
That Ann's pregnancy and delivery will go well,
For peace in El Salvador.

Paul did find a job. Not only that pregnancy, but also Ann's two succeeding ones went well.

I have prayed for peace between Palestinians and Jews in Israel, Catholics and Protestants in northern Ireland, Armenians and Azerbaijanis in the former U.S.S.R., Tamils and Sinhalese in Sri Lanka. I have prayed for Buddhists in Tibet. Not all my prayers have been answered yet. So much hunger in the world. Inadequate gun control in the United States. Capital punishment not yet abolished everywhere in the world. *We wrestle not against flesh and blood, but against spiritual wickedness in high places.*

I have seen the Berlin wall come down. I have seen totalitarian governments collapse. Apartheid has crumbled in South Africa. I shall keep praying daily, along with so many others all around the world, that *thy kingdom come, thy will be done on earth as it is in heaven.*

One great thing about being as old as I am now is that I do more have time to pray. And I hereby resolve to be more diligent in my prayer life.

Outside Her Book
Veronica Hilty Lives

What a day it had been! Hannah Hershberger turned her back on the kitchen. She listened to the heirloom clock strike eight P.M. and noted with gratitude that she had two hours until bedtime. Two precious free hours that were to go into reading the new book she was so eager to dig into.

The day had held no open space. It was go-go-go from six A.M. when she began her activities until just now. Jogging. Getting the breakfast oatmeal cooked and served to husband Daniel and herself. Checking her appearance. Would the students attend to what she was teaching, not to some flaw in her appearance? Then the drive to her eight o'clock class, for she was an adjunct professor this term. All morning in the classroom. Some of the same old material. Dangling participles. *Walking down the street, the house was painted blue.* But houses cannot walk down streets. Who was walking? *When I*

9. Does Prayer Work?

was walking down the street, I saw. . . . . A stint of paper-grading in her makeshift office, little more than a carrel in a library basement. A sandwich and fruit lunch. More papers. Lesson plans. Back home by midafternoon. Helping a refugee family fill out forms to apply for permanent residency status. An incoming phone call about a change of time and place for a meeting her husband was to attend; another about a postponed dental appointment. Going through the mail. Writing two checks for utility bills.

So soon it was time to prepare the evening meal. Hannah sometimes wondered, *How much of a lifetime goes into details like grating carrots, answering the telephone, and emptying wastebaskets? Are these humble activities related to, indeed part of, some grand divine design? Or are they cosmically neutral? They are necessary, after all. One should probably take a Brother Lawrence attitude toward them. Can one empty a wastebasket to the glory of God? Only if the contents are biodegradable, no doubt.*

But on this particular night when Hannah flipped off the kitchen light and picked up her new book, she was not puzzling about the meaning of anything at all. She was simply glad the day's obligations were finished at last. Or were they? A nagging uncertainty teased the edges of her mind. Had she forgotten something?

Hannah opened her new book with its tantalizing promise of a mental journey to come and settled comfortably under the reading lamp to enjoy the next two hours. Faintly she heard husband Daniel's saw whirring in his basement workshop and felt a sense of contentment in knowing that he also was having a satisfying evening. On this occasion, however, for a reason she herself would not discover until hours later, Hannah found herself quite unable to concentrate on her reading. The image of her neighbor Veronica Hilty kept flashing into her mind.

"Did I promise to do something for Veronica today? No, I did not." She resolutely focused her eyes on the print once again.

Veronica Hilty, an old Swiss woman, lived alone in an inherited house in the next block of this midwestern village in which Hannah and Daniel Hershberger also lived. Hannah visited her about twice a week, on late Sunday afternoons taking her a copy of the morning church bulletin, for Veronica seldom left her house. On week days Hannah sometimes stopped en route to the post office or grocery and added Veronica's small errands to her own list. Veronica seemed overjoyed and honored at Hannah Hershberger's brief visits, for she had found in Hannah that rarest kind of human being, an appreciative listener.

Veronica Hilty, unmarried and childless, had spent thirty years as a missionary in a West African hinterland girls' school. She loved to tell stories about those years, and Hannah loved to listen to them. Veronica had purchased all the supplies for that school, including food for the student dining hall. She had bargained with traders for rice, soap, oil. She had bought vegetables in village markets. Veronica Hilty spoke Kuranko, Bambara, and Menika, tribal languages, skills totally unappreciated in this small American town. She had preached in one of three native languages almost every Sunday of her thirty years in West Africa.

Hannah Hershberger would sit in the antique rocking chair listening to Veronica's reminiscences, furnishing only verbal exclamation points.

9. Does Prayer Work?

"Really!"

"Amazing!"

"How interesting!"

Hannah Hershberger would think, *Veronica Hilty is my kind of woman. I admire her spunk, her independence, her strength. But here in the U.S.? What Catholic bishop would want a Sister Teresa in his diocese?* Hannah saw Veronica Hilty as a heroine and a saint, but most of her fellow townsmen saw Veronica Hilty as a crotchety, demanding old woman, and they could state their reasons.

Veronica at various times had arthritis, asthma, backache, legs that refused to function, numb fingers. Yet she constantly rejected medical advice, convinced that the town's two young doctors were quite incapable of understanding her body. "He put me on prednisone, and I can't take prednisone. That's what did it! He's not helping me one bit," she would complain sharply. She substituted her own remedies for those prescribed by the physicians—garlic, honey, and lemon juice taken before bedtime, grapefruit and goats' milk, or some other amazing concoction. Veronica Hilty called up the village fathers to complain that the neighborhood children had stopped up the drain to her septic tank by stuffing a washcloth into it. She curtly dismissed a visiting nurse who dared open her kitchen cupboard doors. She often called her good-hearted niece, who lived fourteen miles away, and expected immediate chauffeur service to the bank or drugstore.

But all this time you have been hearing about Veronica Hilty, Hannah Hershberger has been sitting back there in that living room with her new book at the end of a busy day trying without success to receive meaning from the printed page. Instead she has been getting wave after wave of Veronica Hilty.

110

At last she puts down her book and looks at the telephone.

Hannah stood up and moved hesitantly toward the telephone. "It's already bedtime, really too late to call," she thought. But call she did. She knew Veronica's number from memory. She heard the phone ring at the other end of the line. Once. Twice. Thrice. Then a mere whisper, "I can't talk. I can't breathe."

Alarmed, Hannah quickly jotted a note to her husband, busy in his basement shop, "Veronica Hilty in trouble. Gone to check."

She grabbed her car keys and the wallet containing her driver's license and was on her way.

Hannah Hershberger entered Veronica's unlocked front door and found her wheezing audibly, breathing with extreme difficulty.

Hannah drove her old neighbor to the emergency room of the local hospital.

There trained medical personnel flew into immediate action. They put Veronica on an oxygen-breathing machine and gave her medication intravenously.

Hannah paced about the waiting room, wondering what she should do next. Would she need to stay the night in the hospital?

No, in just two and a half hours Veronica Hilty's breathing was normal once again. She could return home. The nurse in charge of the emergency room commended Hannah Hershberger. "You got her here just in time to prevent cardiac arrest."

Aghast, Hannah asked, "Do you mean she could have died?"

"Yes, that's what I mean."

111

9. Does Prayer Work?

Hannah carefully drove Veronica Hilty to her home and accompanied her to her front door. "Should you be alone tonight?" she worried.

"Oh I'm perfectly well again! I'll be all right. You go on home."

The heirloom clock struck midnight as Hannah slid quietly into bed beside her sleeping husband. She breathed an inner prayer of gratitude. "Thank You. Thank You." What a day it had been!

10. How Shall I Cope with Evil?

At Shalom
Hannah and Ada Go To The Art Museum

Shalom Home chartered a bus and took residents who wished to go, on a trip to their nearest major art museum. No one enjoyed the day more than did Hannah Hershberger and her friend Ada Diller. Hannah used her eyes and descriptive powers on Ada's behalf. Ada's appreciation challenged Hannah to see more clearly. The next morning Hannah wrote in her spiral notebook.

Had a hard time sleeping last night because of pain in my hip. Got up and took a pain pill. Was grateful for the elevators and ramps at the museum. The experience was well worth any pain caused by more than usual exertion. Mentally reviewed the paintings we saw. Describing them to Ada was certainly challenging. Just what color are Van Gogh's wheat shocks?

And how could I ever describe accurately that crowded Pieter van Bruegel the Elder canvas on loan, "Massacre of the Innocents"? All those soldiers, horses, dogs, and above all, distraught parents and children. A dead baby on the lap of a weeping woman.

After prayerfully reviewing the entire day, I prayed the Lord's Prayer slowly, especially meditating on *Thy kingdom come* until I fell asleep.

10. How Shall I Cope with Evil?

Hannah closed her journal and put it into her lower left desk drawer. Then she stood, set up a toppled-over picture of her two Boston grandchildren, and sipped ice water from her thermos mug. She surveyed the one room, now her comfortable home, carefully furnished with her most cherished possessions—a flower garden quilt, a paperweight, a desk, an old wedding certificate, a wood inlay picture of a tree. Then, still thinking about the Pieter van Bruegel painting she had seen the day before, she sat down once again to write.

Inside Her Book
Hannah Searches Her Soul

I cannot comprehend the magnitude and scope of the evil that has occurred in this my century, the tortuous twentieth. *The Gulag Archipelago.* *"Whole nations dumped into sewage pipes,"* as Solzhenitsyn put it. I could hardly bear to read his book. Tens of millions killed in the Stalin years. The Holocaust. Six million Jews exterminated at Auschwitz, Belsen, Buchenwald. Obliterated from the face of the earth. Up in smoke. *Oh the Chimneys!* (Surely *The Diary of Anne Frank* will be one of the remembered books of this century.) The fire bombings of London, Dresden, Tokyo. The atomic bombings of Hiroshima and Nagasaki. Cambodia and the atrocities of the Khmer Rouge. Corpses piled up like pieces of wood. People simply disappearing in Argentina and Colombia. Famine in Africa. Bloated bodies. Stunted children too weak to cry. Over and over in my century, *massacre of the innocents.*

The cumulative weight of so much woe, pain, death, discrimination, hunger, rape, injustice, imprisonment is just too much for my mind. To comprehend it fully would be to be crushed into insanity. Although I cannot begin to comprehend this great ocean of twentieth century pain, I have on occasion glimpsed a single individual's share of it. Survivors do not tell their stories easily. Many months of deep trusting relationship precede such a telling, for old memories can be too painful to speak about. But I have noted that telling one's painful story can be healing.

I have listened to people who lived through World War II bombings in London, Tokyo, Berlin. I once met a survivor of Auschwitz. What appreciation she had for life!

We entertained in our home Dr. Tatsuo Matsumoto, once principal of a girls' school completely destroyed in the Hiroshima bombing on August 6, 1945. He told me he saw his dead wife floating in the Ota River, her hair spread out on the water, and thought of Ophelia. Dr. Matsumoto had white radiation blotches on his skin. He had a spirit utterly loving, forgiving, beautiful as Mount Fuji itself.

I once taught English to a young woman who bore her first child in Pol Pot's Cambodia. She was forced to tie that newborn on her back and go out into the wet paddies to plant rice. Her baby died. It is a wonder she lived.

Human beings long for a scapegoat on whom to blame evil. Hitler, Stalin, Pol Pot, Mao, Ceausescu, Noriega. How hard it is to accept Solzhenitsyn's observation that the line between good and evil is drawn through every human heart. *There is none righteous, no, not one.* That includes me. I too am a cause of evil in the twentieth century.

10. How Shall I Cope with Evil?

All my life I have wrestled with the problem of how to deal with the ocean of wrong. Where does one begin? Surely not with the ocean of evil itself. That would be to drown. My grandfather used to say that the Apostle Peter could walk on water when he kept his eyes fixed on Jesus, but he began to sink when he looked at the waves. I too would have sunk long ago if I had concentrated on the waves of evil rather than looking at that saving gaze of the Lord Jesus. And I must have faith to believe that *an infinite ocean of light and love is flowing over the ocean of darkness and death.*

Another Bible story that instructs me is that of the little boy who gave his five loaves and two fishes, all that he had, to Jesus. What more can a single individual do? I have to believe in the miracle of the multiplication of loaves and fishes. The alternative is utter despair.

A worn sheet torn and rolled into bandages. A layette for a newborn baby. A school kit for a child in a war-devastated country. A letter generated by Amnesty International on behalf of a prisoner. A phone call to a legislator about a bill that would improve life. Urging friends to support gun control legislation or the peace tax bill. An unsuccessful attempt to get a dedicated, capable Christian neighbor elected to the U.S. Congress. A blanket. A cup of cold water. A meal served to a stranger. These have been my loaves and fishes. That is all I have ever had. I have never had enough money to make a really substantial financial gift to any good cause. My tithe has gone out in little dribbles.

I look back over my lifetime and wonder about the way I spent my time. I do not regret a single hour I invested in our children or in the church. But I do wonder about some of those other activities.

Always so many needs and demands. Weighing needs and demands against my twenty-four hours per day, against a limited amount of energy, against skills and abilities. Of all the possible things I could have done, what did I do? I probably frittered and dabbled too much. I have been cub-scout mother, PTA president (and secretary and program chairman). I have held offices and worked on committees for local groups of the Fellowship of Reconciliation, American Association of University Women, Church Women United, and Women's International League for Peace and Freedom. I have chaired and worked on more church committees than I can name. The notices I have placed in newspapers about meetings would probably fill a small book.

Why did I do all those things? Because I was asked? Because I wanted to? Because I considered them contributions to the community? Because I considered them my duty? All of the above? Perhaps I listened too much to outer voices and not enough to that pure voice of heavenly wisdom that moves upon the inner deep. Perhaps I should have concentrated on one good cause rather than scattering my brush strokes across such a wide canvas.

Hannah Hershberger laid down her pen and moved slowly to her window. "This is enough soul-searching for today," she thought. "Soon the Shalom helper will be bringing me my bedtime snack. I hope Rosie Basinger is on duty tonight. I am so fond of that girl. I do hope she will get a job teaching music in a school, although I would miss her very much if she were to leave Shalom. And I must not forget to give her the postcard reproduction of 'The Music Lesson' which I bought for her at the museum store."

Outside Her Book
Santiago Sanchez Escapes Despair

Loneliness cut Santiago Sanchez like a sharp knife. How dreary to wash dishes in that hot dish room at Carrie's Cafe eight hours a day, six and sometimes seven days a week. To hear only the harsh sounds of English beating on his ears. How he longed for the soft, liquid, melodious flow of his native Spanish.

At home in El Salvador girls looked coyly at him. Why not? He knew he was handsome. His black hair curled and shone. His dark eyes sparkled. He danced as lightly as wind in a banana grove. On fiesta nights Santiago savored the sweetness of the village maidens. He could choose whom he wished.

Here in this harsh northern place, no soft girlish glances came his way, even if he now had a mirror of his own and carefully oiled and arranged his curls each morning. He could not look forward to female company after work hours and on weekends. These big, blonde women, looking like ice queens, ignored him totally.

If only he could just drink until he forgot all this harsh reality, the dishroom, the loneliness. But that was out, for the Hershbergers, with whom he now lived, had told him that if he came in drunk again, he would have to move elsewhere.

Santiago liked xylophone music, dancing, cigarettes and beer, prize-fighting, exciting movies. He went to see *Dirty Dancing* three times. But the old Hershberger couple who had taken him into their home liked quietness, going to church, and music that had no beat at all to it. What dull, boring lives they led! Always books, books, books! And church, church, church!

Meanwhile the Hershbergers worried about Santiago. He seemed morose, depressed, uninterested in learning English or in exploring his new environment. He would sit unstirring for hours on their porch gazing into space.

"Would you like to go walking?" No, he was not interested.

"How about doing some woodworking in the shop with me?" No.

"What can we do to get him interested in life?" Daniel and Hannah would ask one another.

The Hershbergers sought counsel. "Give him time." "These Central American refugees have often been severely traumatized. Remember that he was in detention (that's like prison) in Brownsville, Texas, for months." "Healing doesn't happen overnight."

The Hershbergers took Santiago to the zoo. They persuaded younger friends to take him bowling. They drove miles one Sunday morning to the nearest Spanish-speaking congregation only to discover (how foolish of them not to have realized) that simply speaking the same language is not a guarantee of common ties and feelings. Despite their various attempts, Santiago remained often morose and depressed, although the television set did help somewhat.

The Hershbergers had purchased an old black and white television set for Santiago's personal use in his basement room next to Daniel's shop. How proud he was of that television set! Hannah and Daniel were sometimes appalled at his choice of programs. The more nearly naked the women, the more violent the action, the better he seemed to like the program. But the Hershbergers did not curtail his freedom to control the dial as he chose. Perhaps if they could understand better what had gone into his life, they could provide more constructive activities. But what?

Week after week Santiago ate at least two meals a day at the Hershberger table. The three gestured, laughed, and exchanged words. Egg/*un huevo*. Cup/*una taza*. Salt/*la sal*. Daniel always passed Santiago the tabasco sauce, for Hannah's cooking was too bland for him. Hannah made hot chocolate or coffee for Santiago each meal because he liked them so much.

The Hershbergers provided a quiet backdrop for Santiago's life—always there, always concerned about his welfare, patient and unpushing. Gradually the strained muscles on Santiago's face began to relax. Some of his fears subsided. After all, no one kidnapped nor attacked him on these streets, even at ten at night when he returned from his job at Carrie's Cafe. Even so, he kept his knife sheathed and hidden under his belt.

One Sunday noon the Hershbergers invited to dinner the high school Spanish teacher friend who had helped them through many a communication muddle. That day the dam broke, and Santiago's story poured out. The Hershbergers had often wondered about his experiences. How had he come to them? He had neither social security number nor visa. He did have legal papers indicating that he was awaiting trial to determine whether he could stay in the United States or would be sent back to El Salvador.

On this Sunday at last they understood at least part of his story. He told of months of fear and hiding. Young, strong, and virile, he was wanted in El Salvador by both the government forces and the guerrilla rebels for their armies. But Santiago did not wish to join either army. He only wished to work at his milk-delivery job and seasonal coffee-picking to earn money to help support his mother, brothers, and sisters. Why should he fight?

Both armies tried to capture Santiago. As he delivered milk early in the morning, he often saw decapitated and mutilated corpses. What had these unfortunates done to deserve torture and death? Would the same happen to him if he continued to resist?

Santiago's older sister provided him with money for a bus ticket up into Mexico. Eventually he crossed the U.S.-Mexican border illegally, was picked up by U.S. immigration officials and placed in detention in Brownsville, Texas, until church people intervened on his behalf, offering to provide work and support for him while he applied for asylum in the United States.

The money Santiago earned washing dishes at Carrie's Cafe went to the church, which allocated part of it to transportation and bail costs, another portion to the Hershbergers for his room and board, and the rest of it to Santiago.

Santiago, on receiving money, went immediately to the post office, purchased a money order, and sent it to his sister in El Salvador as repayment of her loan to him.

The Hershbergers continued to look for ways to help Santiago to a happier life. Eventually Daniel found a key. Telling his story had loosened Santiago up somewhat, but he still had bouts of depression. Santiago contributed daily to the smooth functioning of the Hershberger household—washing dishes, running the vacuum cleaner, mowing the lawn, washing the car. Never had the Hershberger car been kept so clean.

One day Santiago after many months launched out on his own into the streets of the Midwestern village. He went to a garage sale, that ingenious entrepreneurial invention which enables enterprising villagers to earn a few dollars and get rid of unwanted possessions at the same time.

Santiago purchased and brought to his cramped basement room an old typewriter that typed all twenty-six letters of the alphabet but skipped spaces unpredictably in the process. The next week he brought home an electric toaster. His purchase the third week gave Daniel the clue that proved to be instrumental in Santiago's being able at long last to experience joy in the U.S.A. Santiago brought home a used bicycle pump.

"Why a bicycle pump?" Daniel queried him. "You have no bicycle."

Santiago straightened his spine, lifted his head, and said with a glint in his eye, "Some day I have bicycle."

Daniel read the classified ads in the local newspaper until he found a used bicycle for sale. He took Santiago to see it. Together the two of them provided the purchase money, and the bicycle became Santiago's. Never was an owner prouder of a possession, whether Cadillac or Lamborghini, than was Santiago of that bicycle.

He smiled secretly to himself as he painted the bicycle red. He had never ridden such a vehicle before. Daniel taught him how to balance himself, and he felt absolutely triumphant when he found that he could manipulate the two-wheeler down the driveway and out into the street. If only the girls back home in El Salvador could see him now, riding his own red bicycle! He asked Daniel to take a picture of him and his bicycle and sent one to his sister.

"Can you believe how that bicycle has changed his life?" Hannah observed to Daniel one evening. It was as though Santiago's spirit could move freely on bright red wings instead of remaining darkly behind invisible bars.

Eventually the case of Santiago Sanchez was resolved, and he was accepted as an emigrant to Canada. Hannah Hershberger tried to think of what to give him as a parting gift and selected a decorative cup out of which he had consumed so much coffee and chocolate at their table.

Santiago rejected her gift, using words she had taught him. "No. Cups are in Canada." He asked for instead and was gladly given the small wall mirror from his basement room.

Just before his departure, Santiago and Daniel carefully tied the red bicycle to the back of the car that was to take Santiago to Canada.

11. Am I Ready to Die?

At Shalom
Another Resident Dies

Shalom Home was divided into separate areas: cottages for independent living; apartments and rooms where residents had the option of either doing their own cooking or eating in a common dining room; care floors whose residents needed help with such daily activities as dressing and bathing; an Alzheimer's unit quite separate from the rest of the complex, and a nursing care floor.

Because of its reputation as a well-run, compassionate place, there was always a long list of persons wishing to enter Shalom as residents. As soon as a bed on the nursing floor or a cottage on the grounds was vacated, someone else moved in.

On a bulletin board inside the entrance lobby of Shalom Home a sign sometimes said We are happy to have known, *followed by the name or names of residents who had died or moved away. The signboard also recognized newcomers.* We are happy to welcome, *and again a name or names.*

At one of Hannah's weekly reading sessions with Ada Diller, Ada told her about a newcomer who was having difficulty adjusting to Shalom.

"She moved into a room here on our wing about a month ago. Yesterday afternoon the aides simply could not find her. They looked in the library, the chapel, the front

125

lobby, the exercise room, everywhere they could think of."

"Well where was she?"

"She was sitting on a porch swing at a home two blocks from Shalom. The people who live there came home, saw her sitting on their swing, recognized her as a Shalom resident, and called the front office. She seemed confused and said she wanted to go home."

"How sad!"

"Yes. May it never happen to us."

The two women continued to share Shalom news, and when Hannah wrote a few lines in her journal, it was to record a death the night before that Ada had told her about.

Another resident died last night. Simon Bauman had been ill and completely helpless in the nursing wing for I don't know how many months. So far as we know, he was unaware of his visitors. What a blessing that he could go!

Inside Her Book
Hannah Contemplates Death

Here at Shalom Home, death is a part of life. We all know that our bodies will one day be taken out of Shalom Home by an undertaker. Most of us accept this with serenity. Sometimes I have prayed that death might come quickly to one who is suffering. Death can be a friend, not an enemy.

As I have grown older, the line between the visible

and the invisible has blurred. Once after Daniel's death I sat on the porch swing and felt utterly depressed and discouraged. I did not want to live anymore. Our children were grown and far way, even Paul and Ann at that time. They did not need me. (Or so I thought. It turned out that they did need me after all.) I had no significant work to do. (Again I was wrong.) I wanted to die.

At that moment I saw Daniel's face. All radiant and shining, like light. It now reminds me of the experience Mary Burton told our prayer group about the death of her sister. Language is simply inadequate to explain what I experienced. I cannot even describe where he was. *Radiance* and *shining* are the strongest words I have for what I saw, yet they are far too pale and weak for the reality, like shadows to the sun.

Daniel's face faded. I stood up, walked resolutely to the telephone, called the church office and asked whether they needed hostess help for the meeting we were having with guests the following Sunday afternoon. I was surprised to hear the confident tone of my own voice. From that moment on I have never longed for death.

But I know that I too shall one day die. Already I have outlived many of my contemporaries. I do not wish to lose my mental and physical abilities at the end. Daniel's death was difficult because it was so unexpected, but I have been grateful thousands of times that he did not need to suffer a long, lingering illness. I certainly do not wish to contract Alzheimer's.

It distresses me to walk along the hospital floor here at Shalom and see completely helpless residents. Will that happen to me? Where are those people? I mean their essence, their personalities. Surely no longer in those bodies.

11. Am I Ready to Die?

Do people die before they die?

I do not wish to lie helpless, a burden to other people. On the other hand, perhaps I should be willing to end my life in exactly that way. What would the human race be like if there were no tiny babies or helpless old people to care for? Our Lord said to Peter, *When you are old, another shall dress you and carry you where you do not wish to go.* Most people think that means Peter was crucified, a tradition handed down in the early church. But it could also mean that he became ill and helpless in his old age. If it could happen to so great a human being as Peter, surely it could happen to me.

If I could choose, I should like to die on Easter morning, as did Teilhard de Chardin. And I should like to move gently and quickly from this life to the next as Daniel did. But I probably have no control over the time and the manner of my departure. I am content to leave it in the Lord's hands. Daily I commit my life into God's care and keeping. I pray, "Prepare me to die without fear. Be with me as I pass from this life into the next."

Hannah continued to think about her book, as she closed its pages. This book I am trying to write seems disjointed and scattered, the way my life has been sometimes. I wonder if I am accomplishing what I set out to do, namely to try to see whether my life has been worthwhile, whether I have contributed anything to the Kingdom.

One of these days I must finish my book, but not yet. *Hannah put the day's pages in the bottom drawer with the others.* Soon Rosie Basinger will be bringing me my nightly juice and crackers. Rosie is definitely my favorite among the young women who work here. She treats me like an intelligent fellow human being, not like a has-been, lacking in mind. Yet she is patient and kind with me when I move slowly because of this stubborn hip.

Outside Her Book
Rosie Basinger Gets A New Job

Rosie Basinger considered her job at Shalom Retirement Home temporary. She really wanted to teach music in an elementary school. When she got her degree and state certification, she placed her name on various lists. Her résumé was on file in the Education Department of her college and available to prospective employers. But teaching jobs were hard to come by.

A graduate without a job, she had to pay rent for the two-bedroom apartment she now shared with a college friend. And she was eager to begin paying back that enormous college debt. Even though it was not her first choice, the job she secured at Shalom Retirement Home at least provided a paycheck at the end of each week.

Often Rosie worked the three to eleven P.M. shift. When she came on duty in the afternoon, her first task was to push a tray cart to all the rooms on the hospital floor and offer residents their choice of juice—orange, apple, prune, cranberry, or tomato. She also filled their water pitchers and did errands for the supervisor. Later she wheeled residents unable to walk, to the dining room for the evening meal.

11. Am I Ready to Die?

Then she spoonfed several paralyzed bedfast patients.

Feeding old Mr. Shoemaker depressed her. With head tilted back and eyes closed, he seemed totally unresponsive. Rosie would say as cheerily as she could, "Good evening, Mr. Shoemaker. How are you today?" No response. None at all. Yet he did open his mouth for the spoon, and he did chew and swallow the food. Sometimes she had to wipe dribbles from his chin.

"Is this how life ends?" Rosie would think. "Will this happen to my parents or to me? What if he were my grandfather?" Rosie's maternal grandfather was no longer living. Grandfather Jeremiah still lived at home with her grandmother, both of them in their late seventies.

Rosie looked forward to eight o'clock when she moved from the hospital wing of Shalom to the self-care floors. On these floors residents lived independently, taking care of their own needs. Again Rosie pushed a tray cart loaded with juices and whole wheat snack crackers. She knocked on doors and offered residents her wares. To the residents this seemed one more service offered to them by Shalom Home. To Shalom administrators it was a way of ascertaining each resident's well-being before bedtime.

Rosie Basinger's favorite resident was Hannah Hershberger up on the second floor of the east wing. "I won't mind getting old if I can be like Mrs. Hershberger," Rosie would think. She usually spent five or ten minutes with spry, inquisitive Hannah, answering questions about herself.

Mrs. Hershberger, for some strange reason, seemed to remember things Rosie told her, unlike some others who did not even recognize her from one time to the next. One night Rosie realized, "In these months I have been working at

Shalom, Mrs. Hershberger has learned all about me. She knows who my relatives are and how much I want to teach music. She even knows about Peter!"

Peter was the young man who took Rosie Basinger out a few times during her senior year in college, totally ensnaring her emotions, then dropped her without explanation and married another girl the day after commencement.

"You are so attractive, so kind, and so young, that you have plenty of time to meet the right man. The Lord will direct you to just the right one. You're fortunate someone else married that Peter," Mrs. Hershberger told her. "I once thought I loved a boy named Peter, but it was only a mirage. Now I have a wonderful son named Peter."

As they laughed together, Rosie thought for the first time, "Yes, perhaps I am fortunate not to be stuck for a lifetime with Peter."

After about a year of working at Shalom, Rosie began to despair of ever finding a teaching job. Then one day early in August the telephone rang. The principal of East Wayne Consolidated wondered whether she was still available. The husband of the music teacher who had been on their faculty for several years had been transferred to another part of the country, and she had resigned rather suddenly to go with him. School would begin in about a month. Could Rosie come in for an interview?

She certainly could.

The principal at East Wayne had studied her résumé and had called the persons who recommended her. He felt assured of her qualifications. During the interview she impressed him with her personality and her eagerness to teach. He offered her a contract.

11. Am I Ready to Die?

Rosie was jubilant. At last, an opportunity to do what she really wanted to do! Instead of spooning food into Mr. Shoemaker's mouth she would be sharing her own love of music with children. She would begin her new job in September. She would spend one more week at Shalom, then take some time to spruce up her wardrobe and make lesson plans.

The day after she signed that contract Rosie smiled with anticipation as she pushed her juice cart down the hall toward Hannah Hershberger's room. She could hardly wait to share her good news.

Hannah was delighted. She wanted to know what questions the principal had asked her during the interview. Would she be teaching both vocal and instrumental? What was the school like?

Rosie's words tumbled out eagerly. "I'll begin work the first day of next month."

As she handed Hannah her nightly apple juice, Rosie was startled at the look on Hannah's face. It seemed to be shining, somehow bathed in light.

"Mrs. Hershberger?" Rosie spoke her name suddenly, then, alarmed, "Mrs. Hershberger?"

Hannah spoke slowly, hesitantly. "I'm so happy for you, but I can't talk now because I feel the winds of heaven blowing across my face."

Her head slumped back, and she went limp in her chair.

Rosie Basinger left her fruit juice tray table and ran to get her supervisor.

Hannah Elizabeth Shrock Hershberger's book was now finished, although not by her own design and timing.

12. The Winds of Heaven Blow

Outside Her Book
Hannah's Children Call Her Blessed

Hannah looked down only briefly at the husk that had been her body and at Rosie, then turned immediately to Daniel, to her parents, to Great-Aunt Mandie, to Uncle John, to all the bright and shining ones. Such music! Such light! Such liquid joy! Such gentle scented winds! She now lived in another dimension.

The Shalom Home chaplain called Paul Hershberger and told him his mother had just died unexpectedly. Paul called the other four immediately—Peter in Kenya, Rachel Susan and Ken in California, Rebekah in Bangkok, James and Michiko in Boston. Her children and grandchildren in California and Boston came as soon as travel arrangements could be made. Neither of the two who worked abroad could be present for their mother's funeral, something they would regret for the rest of their lives. The stateside children arranged for Hannah Hershberger's memorial service and for the burial of her earthly remains beside those of their father.

At the service the five grandchildren sang together one of Hannah's favorite hymns, *Take Thou My Hand, Oh Father.* Paul and Ann's oldest, Phil, a sophomore in college, read a tribute to his grandmother. James and Michiko's young Katie presented a poem she had written. The pastor read

12. The Winds of Heaven Blow

familiar and comforting Scripture passages. *We sorrow not as those who have no hope . . . I am the resurrection and the life. Those who believe in me, even though they die, shall live. . . . In my father's house are many mansions . . . I go to prepare a place for you.* The church choir sang *How Lovely is Thy Dwelling Place* from Brahms' *Requiem*.

Ada Diller spoke to the family after the service, telling them how much she had appreciated their mother's friendship. Rachel Susan and Ken sent tapes of the service to Peter in Nairobi and Rebekah in Bangkok. The siblings discussed plans for all five to be together to honor and remember their mother. They divided their mother's few treasured possessions. Paul took home the walnut writing desk his grandfather had given to his mother on her sixteenth birthday. Rachel Susan received the flower garden quilt. The faded old wedding certificate with red roses, that had been their great-grandparents, was stored in Paul's home for Peter, the one most interested in family history. The dove paperweight was stored for Rebekah. James, who shared his father's love of woodworking, received the "Tree of Life" wood inlay which Daniel had given to Hannah on their fortieth anniversary. They divided their mother's books, including much-marked prayer books and Bibles, several for each grandchild.

On the desk the children found a favorite prayer by 19th century writer Rufus Ellis in their mother's handwriting. *We thank you for the dear and faithful dead, for those who have made the distant heavens a home for us and whose truth and beauty are even now in our hearts.*

Hannah Shrock Hershberger's children arose and called her blessed.

About the Author

For the past twenty-five years Elaine Sommers Rich has been a columnist for *Mennonite Weekly Review,* published in Newton, Kansas. She edited a devotional book for women, *Breaking Bread Together* (Herald Press, 1958) and wrote *Hannah Elizabeth,* a forerunner of this book (Harper & Row, 1964), *Tomorrow, Tomorrow, Tomorrow* (Herald Press, 1966),  *Am I This Countryside?* (Pinchpenny Press, 1981), *Mennonite Women* (Herald Press, 1983), and *Spiritual Elegance* (Bluffton College, 1987). She compiled *Prayers for Everyday* (Faith and Life Press, 1990) and edited *Walking Together in Faith* (Central District Conference Mennonite Church, 1993).

Elaine and her husband, Ronald L. Rich, a retired professor of chemistry, have four grown children and four grandchildren. They live in Bluffton, Ohio.

She is a graduate of Goshen College (BA, 1947) and Michigan State University (MA, 1950). In addition to rearing her family and writing, she has taught part-time at colleges and universities in Indiana, Kansas, Ohio, and Japan.

Throughout her life Elaine has maintained a lively interest in the work of the church at home and abroad and in peace and justice issues.